TIME TO
PICK THE FLOWERS

by

BETTE VICKERS

From the serial by
BBC Radio Humberside

HUTTON PRESS

1987

Published by the Hutton Press Ltd.
130 Canada Drive, Cherry Burton, Beverley
North Humberside HU17 7SB

Printed and Bound by

Clifford Ward & Co. (Bridlington) Ltd.
55 West Street, Bridlington, East Yorkshire
YO15 3DZ

ISBN 9 907033 60 1

For Steve
who held "My Foolish Heart"

FOREWORD

Bette Vickers continues this fourth book of stories of her family which began with her grandparents living in Bridlington at the end of the nineteenth century.

"Time to Pick the Flowers" is the story of the grandchild, Molly, born in Bridlington but moving to Lincolnshire early in her childhood. Molly has what on the surface appears to be a normal childhood with her parents, Rob and Ada. But she was always aware of the undercurrent of tension, of unfinished sentences hinting at their family situation being far from normal. It is only when Molly is married and with a family of her own that she learns the true story of Ada and Rob and, of course, Wilf.

Originally written for BBC Radio Humberside, "Fed Up To Top Attic", "Ha'penny Top and Farthing Tail" and "Time to Pick the Flowers" became compulsive listening for a large audience. Published in book form, with the addition of "Life's Golden Time", the second half of the "Fed Up To Top Attic" radio serial, these stories beginning with Thom and Esther and ending with Molly now have a much wider following, eagerly waiting to continue their acquaintance in "Time to Pick the Flowers".

The publishers wish to thank Mr. Graham Henderson of BBC Radio Humberside for all his assistance and encouragement in the publication of the book, and Mr. John Reveley for the cover design.

CHAPTER ONE

'Abide with me..'. The hymn rang through the tiny Lincolnshire church as the congregation of mourners sang the familiar words, with more gusto than musical ability

'I fear no foe..'. He didn't either.

I began to hum the tune to myself and then other phrases raced through my head—'Halfway up the stairs is the stair where I sit', 'I remember I remember the house where I was born'. No I didn't. But I remembered so many things as I listened to the drone of the vicar as he went through the funeral service.

The words meant nothing. My mind was away, away and over the rolling hills, across the Humber river to the seaside town of Bridlington. Even after all these years I still felt a thrill as I thought of my home town, the town where Molly Clamp was born, the child of a bigamous marriage between this man before me now in a wooden box, Rob Clamp, and my Mam — dear Mam — Ada, the sixteenth child of Esther and Thom Skipton.

I could hear Mam's voice so clearly — "Now then our Molly, you behave yourself and don't cry, not in front of folk anyroad."

Desperately I tried to bring myself back to the scene in front of me, the tableau of the vicar saying things he didn't mean about a man he never knew.

I should be listening, I should be showing some emotions. After all, I was the chief mourner. But it all meant nothing to me. At that moment my heart and mind were free — perhaps for the first time in my life. MY life! More like the life of Mam and Dad as she had lived her life again through me and if I didn't seem to be playing the right scene then she would create one of her own.

But something in me still clung to her memory, to the memory of Granny and Grandad Skipton and, in a funny kind of way, to that bloke Wilf Tanner who had dominated Mam's life.

I thought for a brief moment of Dad. Handsome in an odd kind of

5

way, he always wore a pansy in his lapel. As he left the house he would stoop and with his pearl-handled pen knife, he would cut a pansy and carefully position it on his jacket. He walked upright with a military bearing, a fine figure of a man.

On the whole they would seem to have been good parents, the three of us making up the typical family. Oh! if only folk knew.

The drone of the vicar's voice went on and I had to make an effort to stop myself from smiling as my thoughts soared again to my childhood: penny packets of Woodbines, ha'penny gobstoppers, lucky bags and tigernuts; Notarani's icecream and days on the sands under the watchful eye of Aunt Lizzie with wasps by the million crowding around the jam sandwiches; the joy of being pushed on Dad's handcart to fetch work from the Corporation Yard; being stood on a box to sing for the Sally Army; donkey rides and roller skating down by the forty-foot incline to the sands. Oh, such happy memories.

Outwardly we were a happy family, but inside there was torment and unhappiness that I could not understand — until it was too late. I don't think Mam ever forgave Dad for disgracing her in front of her family, and the whole of Brid. But something kept them toge- ther, and as I looked at the horseshoe wreath before me, I realised it was me.

Mam gave me everything, including private dancing classes, when the brass allowed. Saturday mornings were spent at Kit Hastings' dance classes on Windsor Crescent and Saturday nights? That was when Dad came home, more often than not rolling drunk.

"I'm telling you Rob Clamp, I've had enough. I'm fed up to top attic with you. I should have taken notice of what my lot said and sent you packing. You're a bad bugger," Mam's voice would scream through the house and I would cover my head to drown out the bitterness.

"Go on, hit me." He never did, but she always taunted him.

"Aye, you'd like that wouldn't you, Ada, then I can do another nine months for you." Dad's Suffolk drawl would put a stop to all the row.

In a strange whisper she would say, "Ssssh, the bairn'll hear you."

"Aye, that's all you think on, the bairn. I don't count for owt."

It was an odd relationship. They rowed to the very end yet only sixteen weeks earlier I had been standing in this very same spot

6

behind the coffin that held Mam. Sixteen weeks to the hour and the day Dad had simply gone to bed and died. Did he really love her then? Did he need her stimulus to keep him going?

I felt my husband nudge my arm and I returned to the exercise of the day.

"I cannot say much about Robert Clamp, except perhaps that today I feel we bury a man. Only a short while ago he lost his life partner and I like to think that at this moment they are, as it were, on a railway station greeting each other."

I really had to contain myself at that. Mam was more than likely getting on at him for being late. Or was she with Wilf? I wonder what the vicar would have said had he known the true circumstances. He might not have been so glib.

I stood between two stepbrothers, but to all intents and purposes I was an only child, at least the only child of Rob and Ada Clamp. 'Halfway up the stairs...': these words seemed to epitomise my life. A life in limbo, neither one thing nor the other. When I became too bewildered, I would go and sit on the stairs, staring into space or humming tunelessly to myself. Sometimes I would lose myself in writing make believe stories in an old exercise book. Maybe this is what I should do now, write a story as I always said I would. But this one was far stranger than fiction, no make believe story this.

I pictured Thom and Esther from the photograph in our front room taken on their Golden Wedding. They looked so happy and, even at that age, so in love. I thought of Wilf Tanner. His picture had dominated our front room for many years, and I felt a soreness for the heartache Mam had gone through.

All these thoughts, all the whisperings I remembered as a child, and all the hidden innuendos. Perhaps they had all made me a rather precocious child.

"She's got a head on her like an old woman," was a familiar family statement. And it was a big family, in spite of my being an only child. I was loved by an abundance of aunts, uncles and cousins. From Mam's side, though. She "Never had owt to do with his lot". Maybe she would have understood more if she had.

But there's no doubt that without Mam's 'lot' my life would not have been as rich and happy in memories as it is.

Mam always wanted a boy, one that she could call after some bloke who had been killed, the one hung on the front room wall.

Thomson Wilfred, that's who I was supposed to be. Thomson after my Grandad Skipton and Wilfred after this bloke. It seems that the odds were for me being the reincarnation of these two men who, according to Mam, were as damn near perfect as any human being could be.

For the first five years of my life I was dressed as near to a boy as Mam could get, without putting me in boots and breeches. I had short hair with a fringe that good old Aunt Letty had insisted upon.

"For God's sake, why don't you shave her head altogether and have done with it. She'd be a bonny bairn if only you'd let her be", she would say.

But Mam would not give an inch about the boy's clothes — boy's overcoat with a leather buckled belt, lace-up brown or black brogue shoes, and kid gloves with a button fastening. All this lot was topped with a dark velour hat pulled so well down over my eyes that it was the biggest wonder I didn't fall over my feet. I could hardly see daylight!

"She looks just like a manure heap in that lot. Here, lift her hat up a bit or she'll finish up in York Blind School." Good old Aunt Letty again. Any party dresses I had were made by her stitching away on the old treadle sewing machine that had once belonged to Granny. Albeit they were cut down from my cousin Babs cast-offs, but they were so beautifully made that they didn't feel a bit second hand.

Not that there was anything second hand about my childhood. Mam gave me a private education, when the money allowed. I had dancing, singing, elocution, ballet, and piano lessons — all private.

"I don't know what the hell you want from that bairn, honest I don't, Ada, treating her like gentry," Dad would say.

"Well, we all know what you would spend your money on, don't we? A pint pot up at the Black Lion," came the snappy rejoinder.

And he would, too. But Dad did have a point. On the one hand I was being brought up like a lady and on the other? Well, that was something else altogether. A drunken father who had a strange, suspicious air about him and who mixed with all the wrong folk — pub folk. And a Mam who seemed on edge all the time who spoke of her marriage lines, whatever they were, at every twist and turn.

"I can show you my marriage lines," she would say for no reason at all. And it wasn't until many years later that I learned just how much those marriage lines meant to her.

8

I got so confused that at one point I tried to convince myself and everybody else who would listen to my ramblings, that I was adopted, that I actually came from a very ordinary family and my parents had both been killed.

Oh, how I longed to be ordinary and to get away from the situations that engulfed our whole lives. Away from the rows and from Dad's drinking which always made him look such a fool.

"Amen." It was over, the service was finished. Pete, my husband, ushered me to my place behind the coffin and we followed it to the small graveyard.

"Ashes to ashes...". I felt my throat go dry. All this misery, all this time wasted. And for what? Why had they married? Respectability for me? They needn't have bothered.

But I wouldn't have missed any of it for I was never bored. I took notice of all that went on, the sayings and habits and I stored them in my memory box.

Maybe I should write that story after all. But a lot of water had to flow freely before I could actually put it all down in black and white.

Now is the time to open that memory box.

CHAPTER TWO

The very first recollection I have is of being pushed down St. John Street in Bridlington in a large brown pram. I was being taken to a football match. Most of the family were ardent supporters of the local team, Aunt Lizzie in particular. She would take me along and I enjoyed the fresh air, the fuss made of me and the goodies I found being pushed into my mouth. They sometimes did this whilst I was asleep and almost choked me, and I smiled gratefully, if somewhat startled. But I hated football, or any other kind of sport.

Aunt Lizzie never missed a match. Maybe it was a cheap afternoon's entertainment to relieve her life, and she certainly deserved that. She and her family were some of my favourite relatives. She was quite a woman was my Aunt Lizzie. Left a widow with a young family, she worked her fingers to the bone to provide full bellies and warmth for them all. Maybe worldly goods were in short supply, but they had a wealth of love and loyalty that money could not buy.

It was through Aunt Lizzie and ruddy football that Mam got the idea of sending me to school.

One Saturday, a local Derby day, Aunt called and, without a word, put on my coat and hat, plonked me in the pram and pushed me through the front door.

Now, I knew that Aunt Letty was coming and she and Mam were going down town which meant a cup of tea and bun for them and an icecream for me. I preferred that to football.

Thinking myself very wise, I didn't say anything until we were well down Queensgate. "I'm very cold, I want to go home," I wailed.

"I'll warm your backside with my hand," Aunt Lizzie threatened. Our family was always very gentle with words.

I laughed, confident she would never carry out her threat. "I feel sick," was my next approach.

She stopped and looked down at me. "Are you having me on?" she asked

10

And at that point I wasn't too sure. I had become such a good actor that most of the time I could convince myself I felt as I said — cold, sick, or whatever.

Aunt Lizzie decided not to tempt the devil and turned back home. Halfway towards home I began to think the match might be better as I remembered the goodies I usually got.

"It's all right, I feel better now," I smiled.

Aunt Lizzie didn't. "Never mind what you feel, you're going home." She rushed up the street banged on the front door and with a great shove I was through it and halfway up the passage. "She's started playing up and I'm not having any of it."

Mam made to grab me and, with great expertise, I dived past her into the kitchen. My aunts would never lay a hand on me, but Mam was a different kettle of fish.

"You knew I wanted to go down town with Letty. I wanted a hat for Armistice Sunday. You little bugger, you can just lay down there and go to sleep. Your Dad can have you this afternoon."

That did not appeal to me at all. He might be drunk — he would be drunk — and I didn't fancy that. But Mam laid me down on the old settee and threw a coat over me.

"Now you settle down or I'll bray your backside," she said with some force, and made the mistake of clipping my ear.

I closed my eyes and in the blackness began to think all sorts of things. Mam would be sorry if I died whilst she was down town, or if I got blinded like that bloke down Havelock Crescent who went about tapping his stick on the kerb.

I listened as Mam opened and closed the drawers as she got ready to go out. I was alone in the kitchen and I opened my eyes and peeped over the collar of the coat. I spotted the pepper pot and I remembered that Mam had said pepper blinded you. That would do it! I would be blind and she'd be sorry for the rest of her life.

I crept over to the table, took off the top of the silver pot and with a swing threw it back into my eyes. I screamed for it hurt more than I'd bargained for. Nobody told me being blind was painful. I heard Mam coming downstairs and I shoved the offending pot underneath the plush cloth.

"My eyes have gone funny. I can't see. I'm blind!" I screamed and it was the truth. I could not see a thing.

Mam screamed in unison. "Oh my God. I didn't hit you hard.

11

Here, come on hunny." She grabbed me and held me close. I was now really in pain and Mam could see this. She decided to bathe my eyes with boracic powder.

"I'll get them clear and then we'll go down to afternoon surgery. Don't tell him I clouted your earhole." I began to think I might be on to a good thing after all.

In the middle of bathing my eyes, Aunt Letty arrived and at first she too panicked. But fate stepped in and dealt a bitter blow. I began to sneeze with such force that I almost blew her hat off.

"Just what have you been up to young lady?" she asked, looking at me most suspiciously. She lifted up my jumper and sniffed and then began to sneeze too. "That's pepper. You little monkey, it's..." She sneezed again.

Mam stopped the medicinal bit and turned purple which meant a hasty retreat for me and I ran to hide behind the settee.

"Well, you shouldn't be so cruel. You hit me on the head, and you lied. You said pepper would make me blind and it hasn't. I can see."

Aunt Letty started to laugh, but Mam was wild. She charged behind the settee and brayed my backside until it bled buttermilk. This time I went upstairs without a murmur. The battle was lost.

As I listened to them talking downstairs, I began to feel sorry. I was missing one of their gossips, which I loved, especially when they spoke in a whisper or spelled out a word. These were the really juicy bits.

Mam's favourite was her "terrible operation" when "everything was taken away." I thought she was hollow, which didn't please her at all when she found out, in public as usual.

We were all having afternoon tea at the Promenade Cafe, eating cream cakes and toasted teacakes, when Mam stopped and said she wasn't having any more or she'd get too fat.

"Well, you can't say there's not room in there," I piped up, tapping her ample stomach.

"Now what are you on about," she sighed.

"Well, with you being hollow after everything was taken away," I said in my penetrating voice. Another hasty retreat and another clout. But all these little things seemed to give everyone else great pleasure.

Lying upstairs, I was regretting my hasty actions. I wanted to get back in Mam's good books and racked my brain to think of an idea.

12

Of course! She'd not been able to polish the front room floor this week. I would do it. She always said that red japan lino was a sod to polish.

Quietly I went down, into the cleaning cupboard and looked for the polish. Brasso was the first thing to hand. This would do. Mam always got the brass gleaming with this. I went into the sitting room, got down on my hands and knees and spread the white liquid over the floor. But it did not work out as I had expected. It dried all white and got into the cracks.

I heard footsteps on the stairs, a shout, Mam's footsteps hurrying down the stairs, the door being pushed open and the voice again. "Now what? What the hell? Oh my God! I'll kill you Molly Clamp I will. Just look here our Letty. I'll murder her."

Aunt Letty's face was a picture of astonished bewilderment. Mam's face was purple. And me? I was past caring.

"Don't get on to her any more, Ada. Leave the bairn alone. She's too far on, that's her trouble. She's with old folk too much. She wants to be at school."

How could Aunt Letty do that to me. I sat back on my legs and sighed, trying hard to keep back the tears. "It strikes me some folk are never satisfied," I said.

I didn't like the sound of school. Nobody I knew said anything good about school and I wasn't going, not for anybody.

CHAPTER THREE

When school was first mentioned, we were still living in the old house with Brinners. Everything there seemed old, including the Brinners. It had an air of fading, musty dampness and I was very sensitive to things at that time — smell, atmosphere and feelings.

But they were nice people and put up with a lot from me. I was noisy, although quiet when they wanted me to perform, and always around with my big ears at the wrong moment.

When Mrs. Brinner heard of the polish incident she said, "All she wants is occupying. Her brain works too fast for her body. It makes her nerves go forty knots an hour."

Mam thought this a very profound statement and decided that only the best would do for our Molly's brain. She would be privately educated at the convent.

I sensed that plans were afoot. At first with all the whisperings, I thought they were going to carry out the old threat of putting me in a 'home for naughty girls'.

Aunt Letty did not approve of the private part of the education. "Why can't she go to Oxford Street with our lot?" she asked.

"Because I want her to have the best. The bairn was born into enough trouble, I want to do my best by her," said Mam.

'Born in trouble'? What on earth could that mean? I often sensed and overheard people talking about me. "Lovely bairn that. Pity they aren't wed yet. He's still got a wife in Sheffield or somewhere. Bad business that."

Usually I would ask Mam if I did not understand anything, but I had a highly developed sixth sense that told me this bit was better kept to myself. I didn't want to hurt Mam. It was the first chink in my armour, the first brick laid in the wall I began to build around myself.

Mam disappeared on two afternoons and then I was taken up to the convent. On a Wednesday afternoon, in all my mud pie best, I was taken for inspection.

"Why can't I go to Oxford Street?" I asked.

"Because I say not. You be a good girl now and speak nicely and remember your manners or I'll give you a good hiding."

The school building was dark and overpowering. I remember the colour brown, like my clothes. Oh, well, at least we matched. But the colour was the only match we had. From the first moment I set foot in school I hated every moment and became determined to leave as soon as I could.

I was wary of the nuns, floating about in long black clothes. The place smelt a bit like fireworks night, but I looked at Mam's face and decided to behave myself. I could see that this was important to her.

I didn't have to remember to speak nicely because no one took any notice of me at all. I wondered why they had got me there. It wasn't going to make a blind bit of difference how I felt. They'd got it all worked out.

"Is the child to be known as Clamp, or what?" the Mother Superior asked. Mam frowned as if she was going to have one of her 'telling 'em what she thought' turns.

"I'm Molly Clamp, that's my name isn't it, Mam. I'm not 'or what."

Mam jumped nervously, but I saw the twinkle in her eye. "That's right 'unny, your name's Clamp." She gripped my hand tightly and bid them goodbye.

I felt she had been hurt by the questions. I wanted to hurt them back and to know why. I took a last look around before we left.

"I tell you what missus," I said with pursed lips, "I hope you give this place a good wash with carbolic before I come to school. It smells like Ireland's aaar..."

Mam almost threw me down those stone steps. "Why did you have to spoil things by saying that? I sometimes wonder what'll become of you my lass."

The next stop was to Machins to get the uniform. Mam loved it all — gymslip, blouses, tie, velour hat and band, and two pairs of fleecy lined navy blue knickers with a pocket on the right hand side for my hanky, and black woollen stockings.

I didn't reckon much to it. "This collar makes my neck itch," I grumbled.

"You just shut up and think yourself lucky to be going to a private

15

school. You'll never get a better start in life. Many would change places my girl and just you remember it."

"Well, they can for me," I snapped.

The lady serving us laughed out loud at Mam and me arguing and as Mam raised her hand to clip my ears said, "Nay, Ada, don't hit the bairn. By hell, she might not look like you, but she's a real chip off the old block. I can just see you now at her age, you and young..." Her voice trailed off, and Mam sighed deeply. It was all a mystery to me.

I began to worry about the word 'private'. I had only known the word when it was on doors that were kept locked. Were they going to lock me up? Was that what 'Private Education' meant? As I lay in bed, the whole thing became a nightmare. I didn't want to be locked up. Locked up meant dark places, caves and dungeons. I wasn't having that.

I decided to leave home and the next morning waited until I heard Dad take Mam's cup of tea and got myself dressed, lying under the covers until I heard him close the back door.

Quick as lightning, I picked up my little red attache case in which I kept my pencils and exercise book and left the house, racing down the road to Aunt Lizzie's. She always said there was room for one more, she'd take me in.

I banged on the door and it was opened by my cousin Joyce. "What the...?" she spluttered.

"I've left home. Mam's sending me to a private school where they lock you up and I'm scared so I've run away."

I did not get the reaction I expected. Joyce laughed and called out to Aunt Lizzie, "Just look what we've got here — Orphan Annie."

Aunt Lizzie came downstairs in her voluminous white nightie and stared at me.

"She's left home. Reckons she'll be locked up in that private school."

I thought it unkind when Aunt just laughed and said in a very non-caring way, "Well, there's a thing. Get yourself in then. You can stop if you want. You can help about the place. I'll be off to work in a few minutes and when lasses have gone, you can do pots and tidy up a bit."

This didn't sound right at all.

"Good, if she washes up I shan't be late for school for once,"

16

Doris chimed in as she entered the tiny kitchen.

"On your way down, call and tell Aunt Ada she's here. Tell her we'll call for her things later."

My mind did a swift about turn. I wanted to go home, private school or no private school. "I'd better come with you, just to see that Mam's all right without me."

"Oh, she'll not miss you. She'll be glad to get rid of you."

I began to cry. "Oh come on. I'll take you home, but I wouldn't be in your shoes for a pension." Aunt Lizzie got dressed and I was fed hot buttered toast and milk.

I thought it a bit funny that Mam hadn't been to look for me. Surely she must have missed me by now. "If she clouts me hard I'll tell cruelty man, I will," I bawled.

"If she's any sense she'll fetch him herself," Aunt said, as we set off.

I thought I saw Mam just round the corner of South Back Lane, but she disappeared too soon for me to be sure. I began to worry. Maybe she'd really put me in the home for naughty girls now. Aunt knocked on the door and walked in. Mam was stood at the sink filling the kettle. I noticed she was dressed and her raincoat was on the back of the chair.

"You've come back then have you? I was just off to police station to report you missing." She spoke casually.

"Reckons she's left home. Wants to live with us. I thought it best to let you know," Aunt said.

Mam didn't bat an eyelid. "I'll get her things then. Let's have a cup of tea first. There's no hurry."

They ignored me standing there clutching my little red case.

"I might let her bed to one of the bairns from the home. They'll be glad of all her toys and things."

My lip trembled and I began to sob. "I don't want to leave home, I want to stop here with you."

"You went of your own accord, my lass. I've a damn good mind to make you stop."

"I don't like that convent," I whispered as I tried to get on Mam's knee.

"You'll be all right once you get there," Mam said relenting a little.

"I don't know why you're sending..." Aunt didn't get a chance to

17

finish for Mam jumped in with, "She's going and that's flat. For once she'll do as she's told and if she doesn't like it then she'll ruddy well lump it."

And that was that. I decided, for the time being, to lump it like cats do dumplings!

CHAPTER FOUR

That first morning I tried everything, but all to no avail. Mam made up her mind to ignore me and just paid attention to getting me dressed.

"It's not for long. You'll be home at dinner," she said as she left me on the stone steps and pressed the bell.

As the great doors squeaked open I was absolutely petrified. When they banged shut behind me I was almost in a state of coma. I stood in that big hall, not knowing a soul. Didn't anyone realise I'd never been on my own before? I felt lost and scared not knowing what to do or what was expected of me. Then I saw a nun coming towards me.

"Come along Molly Clamp. Come in here and meet all your little friends."

She took me into a room where there were rows and rows of desks with gleaming brass inkwells. Someone dressed all in white was trying to light the fire. She looked like a ghost with her black streaked face.

"Don't you look at the fire, Molly Clamp, or you'll put it out."

I suppose the remark from the nun was meant to tease, but I felt hurt. Why should my face put a fire out? Tears came to my eyes.

"Now don't be a cry baby," she said as I struggled to get my hanky from my knicker pocket.

"I'm not," I sniffed.

"Not what? You say 'sister' when you speak to me." Her tone was sharp.

"You're not my sister. I'm an only one. Mam didn't want any more when she saw me." I trotted out the saying I had heard so many times.

"I'm not surprised at that young lady. I know I am not your sister, but I am a sister in the convent. I am Sister Marie."

It was all double Dutch to me, but I decided to keep quiet. The

19

room was filled with other children, some obviously used to school and others, like me, very new. A girl called Dinah was sat next to me and as she looked rather nice I tried to be friendly.

"I'm Molly Clamp. Do you want one of my goodies?" I pushed forward a crumpled bag of sweets.

Dinah turned up her nose and looked away. "I'm not allowed sweets, thank you." Her voice was what our lot would call 'toffee nosed and trying to put it on'.

"What are you talking all plum-gobbed for?" I asked, but before she could reply that Sister butted in.

"We don't allow sweets to be brought into school, Molly. Give them to me. We have our own tuck shop."

I handed over my sweets and felt in my pocket for my remaining halfpenny. It was still there. I would try this tuck shop at playtime.

Sister Marie was very surprised when the lessons started for I knew most of my basic numbers and could write them down. My big cousin Kenny had shown me how, and I knew my ABC and, with a little help, could write my name.

"That's quite good, Molly. A bit crooked, but a good start."

"Well, you can read them, so they must be all right," I snapped. I was fed up sitting there dressed up to the nines just to scribble. I could do that at home.

By the end of the morning I desperately wanted to go to the lavvy, but I didn't know where it was. I'd watched the others putting up their hands and asking for things, and so I did the same. For what seemed an eternity, Sister ignored me until finally I could not stand it another minute. Tentatively I said, "Please Sister?"

"Well, what is it, Molly?" she finally asked.

"I need the lavvy."

Sister gazed long at me from over the top of her round horn-rimmed glasses. "That is a very rude way of asking to be excused. You may go when you ask properly."

This really baffled me. I didn't want excusing. I hadn't done anything wrong. I only needed the lavvy, before I had an accident. Not knowing what to do, I spent the rest of the morning with legs tightly crossed and breath held.

When the bell finally rang, I rushed into the cloakroom and felt a trickle run down my leg. I was mortified. I heard Sister shouting that I must go back for prayers, but I wasn't interested. I had wet myself and Mam would kill me. Tears rolled down my cheeks and my sobs rang through the cold concrete of the cloakroom.

"Now, now, what's all this?" It was a kind voice coming from behind the rows of coats.

"I've wet myself. That Sister woman wouldn't let me go to the lavvy and Mam'll kill me now." The words tumbled out between heavy sobs and as the voice appeared and I saw it was another of them, I backed away.

"Oh, don't let that worry you. Come along, I'll find you another pair of knickers. It happens to all of us."

This amazed me. She looked too old to do things like that. "Have you done it then?" I asked, just to make sure.

"Many times. Oh, hello Father," she said and turned to a man dressed all in black. What was this Father-lark then? He didn't look that old.

"Is this a new one?" he asked very kindly and smiled at me.

"Yes, and I'm afraid we have had a little accident. But I told her it happens to the best of us."

Father smiled and patted me on the head. They chatted to me, asking my name, and she found me a pair of dry clean knickers to go home in. Taking my hand in hers and holding it tightly, Mother Superior, as I learned she was, led me to the front door and opened it.

"Now, remember what I said. You're not to worry. It happens to us all."

I smiled and waved to her. She was nice. I began to skip down the High Street and then saw Mam just turning the corner. I ran faster, shouting at her breathlessly, trying to say in one word all that had happened to me at school.

"I've been Mam. I've been. And I wet my knickers, but don't you worry. That Mother Superior and Her Dad do it all the time."

Mam stood still in her tracks, and then burst out laughing. What a sight I must have looked — hat on back to front, coat all uneven and waving a pair of wet knickers round my head.

"Good grief, I thought school would tame you a bit. It looks like I was wrong. Come on, let's get you home for some dinner. You'll be the death of me yet."

I laughed with her, for in my innocence I thought that in that one brief morning my school career was finished.

21

CHAPTER FIVE

When I realised that school went on for much longer, I made up my mind to be as difficult as I could. I tried every trick in the book, and more. But Mam's determination was as strong as mine. A battle of wills commenced.

"They're sending me to purgatory," I announced, after spending time in the chapel praying for somebody's soul to be delivered from it.

"Oh, aye. And how will you get there? On Williamson's bus," Mam laughed.

"Where is purgatory? Do you have to be dead to go there?"

"Purgatory is what you give me every day. It's a place for little lasses who don't do as they are told and go to school without kicking up all this fuss."

I had visions of that place, flames and fire, big black holes. I wasn't going there and so for a while I behaved and went to school without any trouble. Mam was certain I was sickening for something.

But all good things come to an end and after a particularly bad morning, during physical training, I rebelled.

I was dressed down to my navy blue knickers and vest, topped by that ugly, horrible garment all girls wore, called a liberty bodice. It rode up around my tummy when I did knees bend and stretch, but, most awful of all, were the black stockings with white garters which wouldn't stay up. I got the idea to roll them down to my ankles and I was bending away in time to the music when the teacher called out to me, "Molly, that is very good. Come out to the front and show these clumsy people how the exercise should be done."

Off I went, swinging away, when suddenly she tapped me on the backside with her ruler. "Who gave you permission to roll down your hose?" she asked.

"Hose?" I didn't know the word.

"Your stockings child. Come here and get them pulled up this minute."

After the exercising my brain was numb and I stood staring at her. She thought I was being insolent and, stepping forward, yanked the back of my pants. The inevitable happened. Snap went the elastic and down went my pants to join my stockings round my ankles. She raised her hand as I bent and side-stepped to miss the threatened blow. As I did, she stepped forward and our feet met, mine clamped firmly on top of hers. She yelled and toppled backwards, falling on the floor with her legs flying in the air from underneath that mountain of clothes.

Pandemonium reigned. I held my pants up around my neck, and danced and screamed and sobbed that it was all her fault. The class were horror-stricken as Sister tried to get up and regain her dignity. She pressed the bell and a novice came to take me out of the way. Firmly she held me under her arms, my legs kicking out in all directions and my mouth wide open. "I hate you. I shall tell my Mam," I screamed.

The novice took me into the kitchen and calmed me down with biscuits and milk. "What's all this commotion about Molly Clamp? You surely are a trouble to us all," she said softly.

"It wasn't me. Sister grabbed my knickers and the elastic bust. She's always picking on me. I'm going to tell Mam."

"You know, I was once a little girl like you. I hated school and anything to do with authority. I went to a convent too, but not one as nice as this. If we were naughty they made us bath in disinfectant to rid our souls and bodies of sin. It made us very sore I can tell you."

I sat open mouthed at the thought.

"After one very nasty punishment, I decided it was a bit silly to carry on like that. I was only making things worse for myself so I decided to be good. At first they didn't trust me, but finally we got it right. I decided to give my life to Jesus and become a nun to atone for my sins and whilst I was about it, to try and make all convent schools a little brighter and happier. Now, how about you Molly, how about giving me and Jesus a promise to try and be good?"

I felt it would save time and trouble if I nodded in agreement. But her words did make sense to my young mind.

When I was taken back to the class, the novice whispered to Sister who actually smiled at me and during prayers asked for Jesus to help

23

me to be good. Everyone turned to look at me, and I felt so daft I nearly cried again.

I was very quiet at home, just eating my dinner and not saying a word.

"What's the matter now?" Mam asked, and I told her the story.

"Did you hurt Sister's foot?" was Mam's only concern. They didn't care about me and I started to cry again just as Dad came through the door.

"Not again. What's up with her this time?" he grumbled.

"I don't know. Maybe I was wrong to send her there. I can't take much more. You can take her back this afternoon."

Neither of us cared for this idea, and as soon as we reached the door of the convent, I started. I kicked and screamed, ran in shop doorways, and hung on to lampposts. Everyone was staring and Dad was getting madder and madder. He desperately wanted to give me a good hiding, but couldn't in front of everyone. As soon as we reached the corner of High Street, he picked me up and with every step until we reached those dreaded great doors, he clouted my backside. He reached the top step and, as if by magic, the doors opened. He flung me through and I sat on the prickly doormat and sobbed. I looked up into Sister's face.

"Well, that was a pie crust promise Molly, soon gone and forgotten."

I stopped crying and concentrated on my shoe laces. I had reached the point of no return. I would be good, and what's more, I'd be a teacher and make school a happy place for bairns, a place they would want to go to every day.

"Sorry Sister. I'm all right now, thank you." I spoke in very civil tones. Brushing myself down I went into the cloakroom and hung my things up properly, and quietly went into class.

I was a model pupil. Sister was almost a nervous wreck wondering what I was really up to. I ignored her snapping and snide remarks and got on industriously with my work. And, to my utter amazement, I found that I was actually enjoying it.

CHAPTER SIX

Each era in life is marked by a milestone, some sunny, some grey, but all, I feel, have a great bearing upon what we finally become.

I found that the decision to enjoy school and to learn as much as I could to become a teacher was one of my milestones. The realisation that something in my background made me slightly different, was another.

Shortly after my reform, I was asked to Dinah's birthday party. I wasn't sure that she really wanted me, but having asked most of the class, she could hardly leave me out. They were well-mannered people.

I was so excited as I had never been to a party before. Mam was pleased too, and was persuaded to let me have a party dress, some white socks, and, best of all, a pair of black patent anklestrap shoes. Aunt Letty made the dress of pink satin with a shawl collar, just like Shirley Temple's. Even my hair was Marcel-waved for the event.

Aunt Letty stood back and surveyed her work. "She looks just like Mam, you know." She referred to my Gran whom I never knew.

On the great afternoon I went to this posh house on Windsor Crescent and was greeted by a man who took my coat. Oh how I wished we could live in a house like this. One all to ourselves would do me. I could hear a piano playing and childrens' voices coming from one of the rooms. They were playing musical chairs and I soon got the hang of it.

Tea was announced and we went into another large room, the like of which I had never imagined in my wildest dreams. Standing in the centre was the biggest table I had ever seen. Over it lay a white lace cloth and over that, well, it was covered with sandwiches, cakes, jellies, and a big birthday cake in pride of place in the centre. We sat down on chairs which prickled the back of my legs, but I didn't care, I was in my element!

I ate potted meat sandwiches, salmon and cucumber sandwiches,

25

and egg sandwiches with bits of green and black in them that I carefully picked out saying, "Don't bother about a bit of dirt, these are fine." Of course they were cress seeds, but I knew nothing about cress. Cakes were next — and then jelly.

"I'll get you a clean plate, miss," said the maid.

"Don't bother about that. This will do fine. Look, I've wiped it spotlessly clean." I showed how I had polished the plate with my napkin, thinking that was what it was meant for. There was a deathly silence and I knew I had done something wrong.

I picked up my plate and mumbled, "Well, if you really think so," and gave it to her outstretched hands.

Everyone giggled throughout the rest of the meal, but for me the party died. To them, Molly Clamp having her sandwiches and jelly on the same plate was a huge joke. To me it was the worst thing I could ever imagine happening.

Dutifully I joined in the games and Dinah's Mam tried to stop the teasing, but I heard her say behind her hand that you couldn't expect anything else with my background. I looked over my shoulder to see if I was showing my knickers or something. What was a background? Seeing my discomfort, she smiled across at me and I stared back. My curls were wilting and hung around my face in damp squiggles. I shuffled on the prickly seat.

"Will you sing or dance for us, Molly?" she asked.

At first I thought to refuse and then defiantly I got up and sang 'On the Good Ship Lollipop' and tapdanced. They were impressed and asked for more, but that was me finished. I sat quietly and waited until Mam came to fetch me.

Back home I asked, "Why don't we have different plates for sandwiches and jelly?" and told them the story.

Mam sniffed and swallowed to hide her feelings. When Dad heard all about it he said that Mam should not have tried to carry such a high head by sending me to a private school. "It just puts ideas into her head, ideas of things she can't have."

Oh yes, I had ideas, but I would have them all, one day. They would see!

The second incident was during the jubilee of King George V. All the kids in town were to attend a tea at the Spa Royal Hall. All our lot were going, but I wasn't all that keen; the word 'party' held only a black mark for me. But they insisted and down Quay Road we went,

26

all lined up in order of age. I was last.

We arrived and stood at the door of the Hall waiting to be let in. Each child had a ticket and number and as we entered we gave our name. "Molly Clamp," I announced.

But before I could get in, a man at the door looked down at me and with a face like thunder snapped, "You're not coming in here you beer sodden bastard!" With that he slammed the door in my face.

My family had all gone in and for a bit I stood in the hope that one of them would come and get me. I decided to go home and walked along the road with one foot in the kerb, hitching and derrying all the way. I'd be better off at home.

Mam was gobsmacked when she answered the door and found me there. "What are you doing here, you've only just gone? Have you done summat," she said, now showing herself to be wearing only her underskirt.

"What are you doing having a wash at this time of day?" I asked. I didn't miss a trick.

"Never mind what I'm doing, what have you been doing is more important?"

"I haven't done anything. That bloke wouldn't let me in because I'm a beer sodden bastard." I spoke the words slowly and deliberately. Mam's face whitened and she sucked in her breath between clenched teeth. "What does that mean?" I looked up at her.

"Don't bother yourself. I'll sort it out."

Dad was now standing at the top of the stairs. He was only half dressed as well.

"What are you doing up there. Have you been having a wash and all?" I asked. He laughed and Mam playfully cuffed my ear.

"Just you listen to this, Rob" and Mam told him what had happened.

"Who'd take it out on a bairn?" he mused.

Mam hummed around a bit and then decided to go down and sort the man out.

Dad was of another mind. "Leave it, Ada, it'll only make things worse. Our day will come."

"What day's that then?" I asked. "And is it bath night or something? You two want to get some clothes on before you catch your death!"

They laughed and I felt happy and warm inside. I liked it when we shared a joke, but I didn't really know what this one was about!

I went and got my exercise book and, sitting on my favourite stair, I started scribbling a story. I would write about today. "How do you spell 'beer sodden bastard'?" I shouted.

Mam flew down those stairs two at a time shouting "Don't you ever let me hear you say that again, Molly Clamp, never." Her voice was angry and I could see that she was choking back the tears. I felt my eyes fill up in sympathy, but if I expected any in return I was disappointed.

"And you can just wipe them eyes. Don't you ever let me see you cry over other folk either. You hold your head up high, my lass. You've nowt to be ashamed on."

I stared up into her set face and nodded. A feeling of triumph came over me, as if a battle had begun, a battle that we would win, me and Mam.

CHAPTER SEVEN

"Our Ada's getting married," I heard Aunt Letty saying.

"What do you mean?" I asked, and was told it was nothing to do with me. Why wasn't it? She was my Mam. What was she doing getting married? I thought all Mam's were married. The gossip then stopped, in my presence at least.

Summer means all sorts of things to me, but none better loved than spending a day with Aunt Lizzie on Carvill's tea stall. I got lemonade, cups of tea, sandwiches and cakes, all in return for fetching back jugs and cups that visitors had left on the sands. I paddled, built castles, with sand and in the air, and even enjoyed a thunderstorm when Aunty would shove me under the counter.

Normally I was terrified of thunder and lightning. I recall one Friday when I was sent down to Brown's on Quay Road for a steak pie and gravy, an errand I loved. During the school holidays you would see hoards of kids with baskets and jam jars heading down to Brown's at half-past eleven. We queued up waiting for the wooden window to open and the rich smell to come through. I was just like a 'Bisto Kid' sniffing away. It was almost a meal in itself. We would get our pies and the gravy in a jam jar.

The skies had looked a bit dull and Mam had said to hurry before the storm broke. I was well forward and quickly got served. Then, hugging the basket tightly to my side and balancing the jar of gravy on top, I set off. The clouds thickened and I heard the distant rumble of thunder. My feet quickened apace. I wanted to beat the storm.

Usually it took a time to get home as I liked to walk steady and stop for a word with Tim, a friendly Alsation dog. He would rub his silky grey body up my leg as I patted his head, and today he wasn't going to miss out on the fuss, storm or no storm. I ran past him without thinking, but he ran after me, nudged my basket and the lot went over. Not for long though. Within seconds he had scoffed the lot in one great gulp.

What with the storm and the thought of Dad's dinner now inside Tim, I was paralysed. The rain came in big droplets, the sky opened, and so did my mouth. We must have looked a sight — me like a drowned rat with Tim still licking the remains of the pie and gravy. I heard Mam's voice and, with eyes still closed, I hurled myself into her arms.

"Come on, then, let's get home. Where's the basket?"

With eyes still closed I pointed to where I thought it might be. She wasn't mad or anything, but sighed and with a smile said, "Come on. We'll go to Grice's and get some fish and chips."

As she was in such a good mood I decided to ask her about the wedding.

"Well," she hesitated, "Well, it's not really a wedding. Dad and I need to sign some papers, that's all."

"Oh, I thought I might be a bridesmaid."

Mam laughed. "You can walk behind me and I'll get you a nice dress." She paused again and then said, "You're going to be christened next Sunday."

"What?"

"Christened, up at Primitive Chapel. It's all to do with these papers. Things have got to be made legal and proper."

The thought of a new frock and maybe a party occupied my mind. I didn't care what the reason was.

I overheard murmurings as to whether "Our Ada was doing right," but when I saw Mam all dressed up I forgot all about that. She looked almost pretty, and Dad cut a fine figure too. There were lots of hugs and kisses and we went back home to a lovely meal.

The following Sunday I was the star and again we had a tea. I began to wonder if we had come into money, if Dad's ship had come in, as he was always promising.

"Well, at least that's the formalities done with," Mam said. So I was a formality was I? At least it sounded important.

But the wedding and the christening did change my life. I can't think how, but from then on changes came thick and fast.

I began to really enjoy school, and I was sent to dancing lessons so that I would have every opportunity to "Make something of myself," as Mam would say.

It seemed that I became the centre of her world and when we moved into 11 Milner Road, well, her cup was really running over.

The only thing I missed when living on Milner Road was my two friends, Hilda White and Trevor Rimmington. What fun we had together on St. John's Street. And what scrapes we got into. The sunbathing one is an instance.

It was a very hot Thursday afternoon and we were playing in the grounds of the Wesleyan Chapel, getting a bit bored and very hot.

"Let's play sunbathing," I suggested. They needed no more asking. We had seen them on the sands, hadn't we? Quickly we stripped off all our clothes, Trevor too, and lay there for all the world to see — in front of all places, a chapel. It had a small grass bank and we lay, turning over and over, and finally rolling down to the railings. But we were spotted and hauled off home in disgrace.

Mam shoved me so hard into my knickers she almost strangled me. Oh, she was so mad, but the crowd that had gathered thought it very amusing. It was bed for the three of us and no meetings for at least two days.

But all that was behind me now. I had new surroundings and new friends.

Milner Road also gave Mam another source of income. She took in visitors. It brought in a nice bit of brass and she enjoyed the cooking. But Dad began drinking again and soon I had to leave the convent, and give up piano lessons. But Mam was adamant about the dancing. Even if we had no food I would go to Kit Hastings!

As Mam and I went home one night around dusk, we heard footsteps following us, someone with a limp. A limp meant someone who was automatically under suspicion and so we hurried. The limp hurried. Mam was out of breath and pulling me along until I stumbled and fell. She whipped round to face the possible attacker and then heaved a sigh of relief.

"Oh, Ralph! I never dreamt it was you. I thought somebody was after us."

"Somebody was, Ada. It was me. How are you?"

He was a well-spoken man, a bit posh, but he smiled and patted my head. "And this is..?"

"Molly," I volunteered.

He smiled again. "I often see you around this time each week. I've moved you know. Just across the way. Have you time for a cup of tea?" He pointed to one of the big houses opposite the Town Hall.

Mam shook her head and looked a bit sheepish. "No. No thanks. I want to get this one home and in bed."

The man put his hand in his pocket and gave me a coin. I knew it was rude to look at it so I pushed it deep into my pocket with a polite, "Thank you."

"What good manners. I see you wisely had her privately educated."

"How did you know that?" said Mam. "But not any more. I think Oxford Street school is much further on."

"And anyroad, we haven't got the money now, have we Mam?"

The man leaned forward and touched her arm. "Is everything all right Ada? Can I be of any help?"

Again Mam shook her head. "Don't take any notice of this one. She says owt but her prayers and then she whistles." Mam tried to laugh and, turning, the three of us walked along the path.

They chatted about folk I'd never heard of and for once I kept quiet and just listened. It was interesting and sounded important.

Mam asked about the practice and I butted in, "I hate practising. I'm glad we've done with piano lessons."

I could not see the man's face, but I felt his expression change. "Ada, are you sure everything is all right? You know I'll be only too willing to help."

"I've said, Ralph. Don't listen to this one. She gets things wrong way round. We're fine."

But she could not bring herself to answer his soft, "Well, good-night then, Ada." She grabbed my hand and set off at such a pace she had me running. We had reached Lawson Road before she slowed up.

"Don't go telling anybody about that man," she said.

I shuffled my feet. I didn't like secrets. "Why?"

"Because .. because you know I've told you not to take money from strangers. You'll get me into trouble."

I was reminded of my wealth and dug into my pocket to bring out a whole half-crown. Wealth indeed. I held it out to Mam.

"No, you keep it hunny. But don't go and spend it all at once."

She was humouring me, but I was quite willing to go along with it. For two-and-six I'd do anything. Well, almost anything.

32

CHAPTER EIGHT

That summer we learned a new ditty, *'Will you come to Abyssinia, will you come,'* the song that told of Mussolini's takeover. It heralded war and 1938 was the last peace time Christmas for six years.

Fashions in toys were changing. Dolls were more sophisticated and had limbs that moved. I was never one for dolls, but I'd set my heart on one of these and a china tea service, for since that fateful party I would spend hours crooking my little finger and pretending to be drinking tea as I had seen Dinah's mother do.

"I told you she'd get ideas above her station. All these airs and graces." Dad had no time for such things. Come to think of it he had very little time for anything unless it was in a pint pot.

But I knew Mam would do her best to get me what I wanted for Christmas because she saved up in Harrison's weekly club. In fact, I knew they were already bought and hidden away in the big wardrobe. I could hardly wait. I would call the doll Mary, after the Queen Mary, and I'd make real tea with Rington's tea and drink it from those china cups.

Christmas for Dad passed in a drunken haze — for me, in a haze of misery and hate. He never went out on Christmas Day itself, he said it was for the family. I think he was too stewed from Christmas Eve to be able to go out. But he had insisted on being Father Christmas and I lay in my bed listening for his voice.

Round the corner it came, singing, "'Nelly DEEEEan'." I heard him bid everyone, including the lamp post, "Good night."

"Well, you're a fine state," Mam said, but not unkindly. After all it was Christmas.

"I'll be all right, Ada, I'll be fine," he slurred.

"Don't break anything or she'll go mad."

"I'll be all right I tell you." He belched, and from that minute I knew he wouldn't make it. I counted each stumbling step on the stairs and I felt each sway as he leaned against the bannister with my precious gifts.

33

As he raised his foot to balance on the top step, he fell backwards and with him took Mary and the tea set.

I flew out of bed and stood at the top of the stairs looking at the heap of my father lying on the bottom step. My eyes came up each step and a remnant of my Christmas lay on every one. The rest lay in a million pieces upon the passage lino. Slowly I walked down and picked up one whole cup and one of Mary's legs, all that was left of the doll.

He lifted his drunken head, opened one bleary eye and tried to say, "Never mind lovey, Daddy will get you some more."

I pursed my lips and frowned, swallowing hard to keep back the tears. Mam held out her arms, but I shrugged her away. "No you won't," I said clearly and firmly. "You're always saying things like that, but you never do any of them. Why can't you be like other Dads? You're just a bag of rubbish, drunken rubbish."

I turned and ran upstairs and pounded the pillow in dry-eyed anger. What could I say to folk now? I'd boasted so much about these presents. They'd make fun of me. They already made fun of Dad and I was so angry. I hated him, I hated Mam, I hated everybody.

Christmas morning dawned and the street was alive with bikes, dolls and prams, skates and scooters. I stayed inside until Nelly Riley knocked on our door.

"You bringing that doll out then?" she asked.

Mam came to the rescue. "No. It was far too dear to play with outside," she said.

I pushed her aside and screwed up my eyes, holding out the remaining leg. "Mam's taking it back 'cos one of the legs fell off. They've given us a bad 'un," and I slammed the door.

"That was clever, Molly," Mam smiled. She was nervous of me, not quite knowing what to say to heal the wound. I didn't cry, there was no real outward sign, but she knew I was deeply hurt.

"What else could I say? Why did you marry him, Mam? Why couldn't I have somebody else for my Dad, like that bloke who gave me half a crown?"

Mam let out a gasp. "Don't you say things like that, my lass. If it wasn't Christmas Day I'd give you a good hiding."

I didn't care. She could do what she liked. Nothing would hurt any more than the way I felt at that moment.

1939 was a momentous year for four reasons — the war, the good hiding, the hospital, and Mam's scalded foot.

Now that I recognised the man called Ralph, I would call out to him as I left school, very casually, and never stopping to talk, mind you. But as I saw him leave his office, I began to think he might be rich. He might be able to help Mam and stop her worrying about getting groceries and paying the bills. I started to wait for the man, dodging until he noticed me.

"Hello," I shouted out.

He smiled and waved me across. "Where are you off to young lady?"

"Home."

"How is your Mummy?" He was very posh.

"Oh, not bad. At least she'd be all right if we'd a bit more brass, and if Dad didn't spend so much time in the pub. She says that if things don't get better we'll finish up in the workhouse."

My errand of mercy over I skipped off, but at dinner time I got the consequences. Mam was waiting at the gate and I could see she was agitated. What could have gone wrong now? I soon found out.

"I'll kill you! What made you go and say a thing like that? If your father finds out, he'll murder you." Each word was emphasised with a clout.

For a minute I didn't know what she was on about and then it dawned. Ralph. He had taken me at my word and turned up on the doorstep just as Mam and Mrs. Copsey were having a cup of tea. Mrs. Copsey thought Mam had got a fancy man and it had taken some time to smooth things over, especially when she heard Ralph mention money.

Mam hit me so hard I couldn't go back to school that afternoon. I threatened to tell Dad and she realised that maybe she had gone too far.

"What does it matter anyroad?" I wailed.

"Nothing. Nothing, I suppose. One day I'll tell you all about it."

My sore, aching backside left my plans for riches somewhat thwarted.

Hospital was something I had only heard of, but an offshoot of the good hiding was a stay in Lloyds Hospital.

To ease the hurt, Mam bought me a cheap sewing set and I stitched away all day. At bedtime I tucked the needle into my jumper and went to get undressed. The needle fell on to the rug and the next morning as I jumped out of bed I planted my left foot straight on it. The needle penetrated right through into the bone.

We were due for a school dental appointment and, in spite of my agony, they went ahead with the inspection. I now know why the old school dentists got such a bad reputation. This one held me down and prodded around my mouth until in desperation I bit his hand!

The school doctor was much kinder and suggested that we see our own doctor as soon as possible.

"You must not lose any time. Lockjaw might set in."

"Lockjaw!" What on earth was that?

Doctor Watson said the same thing and told Mam to have me down to Lloyd's Hospital at three o'clock. She took me home, got a message to Dad and then borrowed Gilly Boldman's pushchair to take me to hospital as by this time I could not put my foot on the ground. I also kept my mouth firmly shut. This lockjaw business was worrying me far more than my heel.

But my silence stopped once they got me into the theatre. Without a word of explanation they held me down and proceeded, without any form of anaesthetic, to try and get the needle out with a magnet. My screams tore through that building and I fought like mad until they gave up and decided to operate at six that night with a specialist brought from Hull.

I was so sore and worried that I forgot everything else until at six o'clock they again wheeled me into the theatre. I shall never forget the kindness of the hospital porter who tried to stem my fears.

"What are they going to do to me?" I whispered, still thinking of my jaws.

"They're going to make you better 'unny," he said and stroked my head.

We entered the theatre and all I could see was white tiles and gowns. A white mask was held over my face and I disappeared down a long tunnel.

Some six hours later I awoke in a little iron bed to see the moon peeping through the clouds. I moved my jaws. They were still mobile! My eyes travelled down to the window to see a familiar face peering through at me. It was Aunt Letty. She had stayed all the time until she could see that I was awake.

"Be a good lass," she whispered and blew me a kiss. Sighing

happily I drifted back into sleep.

They say things all come at once, and that year they certainly did. I had just got over my accident when Mam had one.

She was waiting impatiently for Dad to come home with some money. Tea was ready with the pot on the hob. I was playing outside when a gypsy called. We didn't like them, and to be honest, we were scared of them. Dad was always telling me he would give me away to the gypsies and so I took off when they were around.

The gypsy knocked on our door, but Mam didn't answer. Instead she poked her head through the window and snapped, "I don't want owt. If you'd any sense you'd know I haven't got a damned ha'penny."

"Just a bit of lace, lovey, of half a dozen pegs."

Mam wasn't having any of it, and with a nasty, "Clear off," she shut the window.

It could only have been a second later when screams came from the house. I ran inside to find Mam in the armchair trying to take off her stocking. As she did, the first layer of skin peeled off leaving raw red flesh from her big toe to her knee.

"The teapot fell on it. It just jumped and fell, I never went near it. That bloody gypsy cursed me." She was sobbing with the pain.

The teapot lay on the hearthrug still in one piece, the lid only just ajar. Around it lay masses of tea leaves, but very little water. It was very odd.

Mam's leg was a terrible mess and we had to fetch Mrs. Brumpton who worked up at the Avenue Hospital. As she worked there, although she was not a nurse, she was credited with having medical knowledge. But she was sensible and sent once more for good old Doctor Watson.

"If you hadn't been late home this wouldn't have happened." Mam grumbled to Dad when he finally arrived.

"It's no good going on, Ada. I wanted to finish that job. That didn't scald your leg, but you'd blame me even if I was in ruddy China!"

Dad was more interested in how we were going to manage with Mam having to keep her leg up for at least three weeks. I solved the problem in a few minutes by fetching Aunt Letty. She organised with Aunt Lizzie to call each day and I was to go and live at their house.

I was in heaven. It would be like a holiday and I could work with my uncle in the shed and make things. I could even borrow my cousin's skates. I was almost grateful to that gypsy.

Mam quickly recovered and at the August Bank Holiday weekend I went home. The town was crowded out with visitors. The news of impending war was not good. We really didn't know who or what to believe, but it seemed that everyone was going to have this holiday, come what may.

Near the end of the school holiday Dad took me up to Mrs. Waites' shop to buy some jumpers and a skirt. It was Sunday the third of September, 1939.

As we entered the shop Mrs. Waites held her hand to her lips and whispered, "Come into the kitchen, Blacky. It's Chamberlain on wireless." I could feel the tension and held on to Dad's hand.

"We are now in a state of war with Germany." Those are the words I remember. Dad and Mrs. Waites were almost in tears.

"It'll be a blood bath this time," Dad sighed, and Mrs. Waites nodded wisely.

We walked home slowly, me thinking of our bath filled to the brim with blood, and Dad greeting everyone with the news.

Mam sat at the table with what looked like a half-crown in her hand. "They'll all go and get killed, slaughtered just like last time."

"What's that?" I asked.

"A medal, summat you have to die for."

We, like most of the town, decided on an early night. In the darkness the siren wailed and whined. I called out for Mam and she came and put on the light.

"Put that bloody light out," called a voice.

"Are the Germans here, Mam? Are they going to kill us all?"

Mam held me close. "Not bloody likely," she snapped. I felt reassured. Mam would see to them and no mistake.

CHAPTER NINE

If we had thought the world would change overnight, we were very much mistaken. All we got was a period of absolutely nothing happening with everyone's nerves on edge.

On November 11th, the town held its usual service, but this year it had more meaning. No matter what we were doing, at school or at play, in shops or on the buses, at eleven o'clock on Armistice Day everything stopped for a two minutes silence. When men passed the great cenotaph they would doff their caps in respect. Even the road sweeper would touch his cap. These days were soon to go in the horror of another war.

I took a closer look at the picture on our front room wall. He looked a bonny man, fair haired and smiling. He'd been killed in the Great War, Mam said, and I understood him to be an uncle or something. Now we were at war again, I felt drawn to him.

Men came and dug trenches in the playing fields down Queensgate. I thought the war was going to be fought there. A few weeks later they filled them in again.

And then came the great invasion — of evacuees. If you had room, you had to take them in. A billeting officer visited and decided, you had no say. We got three from one family in Middlesbrough, and what a trio they were. When Mam gave them a bath, you'd have thought she was murdering them, and she swore they'd never sat down to a meal before. From the way they acted, I am sure she was right.

The girl, Maggie, had to borrow one of my nighties and she slept with me. I hated it. I'd never shared before, and I didn't like the look of her, nor her smell. I wrapped my nightie well round my legs and kept to the edge of the bed. As the bed got warmer, I began to share it with other livestock from Middlesbrough. I itched and scratched until I was red raw. It took Mam ages to delouse them all and rid the bed of fleas. She was not at all pleased with that billeting officer!

Our school life also changed. We only attended on half days — mornings one week and afternoons the next. Mam didn't know where she was. The evacuees roamed all over the place and the eldest lad pinched from Maynards shop and Mam had money missing from her purse too.

That was enough. She went down to the billeting officer and demanded that they be removed. The house was a wreck and she spent hours just searching for them. However, she was mollified when told that their parents were coming to visit them.

"See what they have to say, Mrs. Clamp," said the officer, and being a bit sorry for the kids really, Mam gave in.

It must have been awful for those kids, though, being brought to a strange town to live in a house with food at regular times and having to wash and bathe. Having someone who cared for them was something they just could not come to terms with.

On the visit, the parents looked worse than the kids. We gave them a good dinner and they ate very heartily.

"We'll just take a stroll round the town and then come back for tea before we go," said the man. "We'll be back about four, is that all right?"

My mother looked startled. "Aren't you taking the kids then," she shouted after them as they walked down the path. Grudgingly they agreed.

When the pubs closed, bedlam reigned. It was like a circus in Milner Road. The visitors flooded the street, singing, shouting and arguing, most of them the worse for drink.

"Where are the kids?" was the first thing Mam asked.

"Ain't they come in then? What you done with them, you silly slut?" growled the man and gave his wife a swipe round the earhole that would have floored a bloke.

We jumped back in terror, but Mam held her ground. "You can stop that mate. I'm not having that lark here."

He threatened us next and I had to admire Mam's bravery. She shoved me in front of her and shouted, "Don't you hit my bairn, or I'll fetch the police."

It had the desired effect. He backed off and grabbing his wife's arm they left. But our house looked as if a bomb had hit it. Mrs. Ridley came across with much the same story, but she had not been threatened and her house was still pretty much intact.

40

Mam cleared up the mess and called the poor old billeting officer who was in the street seeing to all the other complaints. Mam handed her a small parcel containing their things and told her where to put it in no uncertain terms.

"Are the children still with you then?"

"No, thank God. They took them home, poor little buggers."

And for a few blessed weeks peace reigned, but the blackout stayed to remind us that we were still at war. We saw men in a funny uniform that made them look like convicts and we had air raids during which the whole school would file out into the bike sheds which had been corrugated in to act as shelters.

The headmaster was marvellous with us. He would walk around each group and talk to us to calm us down. He once got me to sing, 'Hands, knees and bumps a-daisy' and when the kids joined in I thought the roof would cave in.

Brid answered the call to arms and one of my most proud and moving memories is of watching a group of young men, mainly teachers, marching down to the station, raincoats over arms and looking so proud. I saw Mam in tears. I spotted Puggy Hawkins and Mr. Garland and I tried to wave to them. Did any of them return? I never did find out.

My home life was deteriorating. Dad was drinking and money was short. He went out to collect a lot that was owing and lost it all on some game or other. I shall never forget that row. It lasted for a week.

"I can't afford to live here without visitors. I'm thinking of asking for an exchange near to our Letty and Lizzie," said Mam.

Dad made nothing of it. He was past caring. And so our next address was 19 Medforth Road, where the rent was cheaper. I watched Mam's face as the furniture was put into the house. We had so much that a lot of it was stored in the front bedroom.

I saw Mam go downhill. She didn't do half the cleaning she had done at Milner Road and her flagging spirits were beginning to show. "I don't know how much longer I can stick this, Rob," she told Dad.

"Well, there's not much I can do, Ada. I can't get the iron I need and that's not my fault. What can I do?" For once he was telling the truth. Iron was rationed out because of the war, but Mam didn't see it that way.

41

"Oh, you'll not do owt. If owt's done it'll be me that has to do it. As long as you've got a pint pot you don't give a damn. I wish to God ..." She spotted me in the doorway and stopped, sighing.

But she didn't wish half as much as I did, and it wasn't for all that much either — just a normal life.

The country was in desperate need of money to build all the armaments. National Savings groups were formed in streets and villages and although the response was great it was felt that a bit of patriotic rousing was called for, a parade perhaps.

I hoped so, for I was now a member of the Salvation Army Sunbeams and I so wanted to march and, most of all, wear a uniform. I felt I would be doing a great deal for the war effort if they would allow me to march through the town in my grey serge dress and hat with bright yellow tie.

There was only one drawback. I had not yet been enrolled, which meant a swearing in ceremony. But my cousin, who was the Captain, was also desperate. Her ranks were not as many as those of the Guides and so on the morning of the parade she decided to have a quick swearing in and I would be given a uniform and could march with them. I was so excited, more so because Mam wouldn't half get a surprise when she saw me at the Priory Church. Not half she didn't!

There was not a uniform of the exact size, so we made do. The result was something that looked as though I had come out of the workhouse. My dress was hitched up round my waist with the belt, my tie reached down to a point between my navel and my knees and my hat, well, it almost drowned me. But with safety pins and help from the laws of gravity, we set off on the parade.

As the beat of the music reached my ears, my feet went. I was marching in step, arms swinging and head held high until my hat fell down over my eyes and gravity gave up on me. Everything dropped, but I kept on marching. I wasn't half enjoying myself.

"Stop waddling like a duck," hissed a voice from behind. I could see the sense in this and from Lloyds Hospital to the Priory I walked with my eyes firmly fixed on the two feet immediately in front so that I could at least keep in step. It seemed miles. Dad was also in the parade, but way up in front with the buffs. He wouldn't half be proud or me — or so I thought.

After the service, as we filed out of church, they spotted me, both

42

at the same time. Mam dived and grabbed me and Dad just blew his top. "She looks as if she's just come from the workhouse," he shouted to Mam and, on reflection, I must admit he was right.

My shirt was now hanging down on one side almost to my ankles and the other side was round my knees. My hat was perched on the back of my head and my sleeves were rolled up like a buck navvy. As I saw their faces I tried, in vain, to hold everything in place, but at that moment the command to attention was given and, being a true Sunbeam, I did so. All my clothing fell into a crumpled heap around my body. I looked, as Dad said so aptly later that day, like a heap of mucky washing.

I was despatched home with speed, laughter ringing in my ears. However, revenge is sweet, for that week I appeared in the local paper, crumpled heap and all. Mam and Dad were not amused.

If Mam had thought that living in a cheaper, smaller house would ease things, she was evidently wrong. Dad was not getting, or doing, the work and she could not supplement the income with visitors any more. And so we took in two more evacuees, this time from Hull, which made everything all right. Well, Hull was almost family, wasn't it?

We got two boys. One left after about six months, but the other stayed and became almost like a brother to me.

By now Dad just couldn't pay the iron bills. He was drinking more and more. I was beginning to feel ashamed of him, and of the way we lived from hand to mouth.

Mam kept saying that something had to be done and she finally took it into her own hands to see that something was done.

CHAPTER TEN

Even Dad had begun to realise that we needed the money more than the pub did and he would come home earlier on Saturdays to make sure that the shopping could be done and we would have food for the week.

One Saturday, Mam had been on edge all morning and when Dad got home she plonked a letter in front of him.

"Another ruddy bill?" he snapped, as if it was her fault. He looked at the postmark. "Lincolnshire?" he said. "Who the hell do we know there?" He opened it and began to read aloud in his slow Suffolk brogue.

"Dear Mr. Clamp, in answer to your application for the post of blacksmith at Laughton near Gainsborough .... What the hell is this all about, Ada?"

"I've been telling you for long enough I'm fed up. I saw this job advertised last week in the '*Hull and Lincolnshire Times*' and I wrote in. I've known nowt but misery in Brid. We can't seem to put a foot right. I reckoned a move would do us good."

"What about the shop?"

"Sell it and good riddance. The money will give us a bit of a start."

"You're not bothered about leaving Brid then and coming with me all that way?"

Mam snorted. "No. I know you are good at your job. I reckon I can manage for the rest and bairn will get a new start and all."

I listened in silence. Go away, leave Brid, my aunts and cousins? They couldn't really mean it.

I was not consulted. My whole world had changed in just a few seconds, and no one had thought to ask how I felt. We all got changed and then went up to see Ginger Jackson who bought Dad's shop and tools. After tea Mam answered the letter and accepted the offer of a job.

For the first time, they were laughing and joking together. Dad

44

stayed at home and they sat listening to *'Band Wagon'* on the radio. I went to bed in a state of petrified uncertainty.

When the family found out, they were wild and could not understand why Mam wanted to leave. But she was adamant and on Sunday 2nd March, after I had played the robber in the pantomime *'Babes in the Wood'*, we left Bridlington at six o'clock in the morning.

Kidd's removed us and as we left Aunt Lizzie's house in the dawning light, I began to cry. In fact I cried throughout the whole journey. They sat me in an armchair at the back of the van and covered me up with coats. I watched the familiar skyline of Brid fade away and felt as if my life had ended.

After what seemed hours and hours we finally drew to a halt. I peeped over the tailboard and saw the village of Laughton. It was covered in snow and frost and looked just like a Christmas card. But oh, it was deathly quiet.

The cottage stood to the left of the road, opposite the cemetary. Dad saw that I was a bit apprehensive and he lifted me gently from the van.

"Here we are, lovey. This is home now."

All I could think of was starting another school, making new friends and the teachers. This was like a foreign land and we might just as well have been in China.

But we were made very welcome. Someone brought a pot of tea and home made scones. I stood watching quietly from the sidelines, legs crossed and too worried to ask for the lavvy. We'd been all through the house and I hadn't seen a bathroom anywhere. If I asked I thought it would make me look daft. Fancy not being able to find the lavvy!

Gladly I saw that Mam wanted to go too. "Where's the lav?" she asked. Dad pointed through the door, over what looked like a forty acre field and down an overgrown path.

Mam looked startled, but getting hold of my hand we proceeded towards what looked like an ice covered little hut. We ran down and pushed open the door. "Bloody hell!" Mam said and then exploded into laughter.

I sighed. It wasn't a lav at all. It was just a shed with a workbench. It looked a bid odd though because the bench had two holes in it.

"Come on 'unny. It's an earth closet, you know, like Aunt Esther's. Come and sit down with me."

I decided upon the smaller hole and sat down, with disastrous results, for I almost went out of sight. My legs flew into the air and I could feel myself slipping down the gaping chasm. Mam came to the rescue. She grabbed my legs and neck and pulled me back to life. My eyes opened in terror ready to cry. Mam laughed again.

"I don't like this place," I wailed.

"Oh, come on, let's sing." And we sat down again and began to sing some of the war ditties. "*'Run rabbit run'*," our voices rang across the garden and as I bent to pull up my pants I saw, through my legs, Dad running up the path.

"For God's sake, shut that door. Everybody can see you," he cried. And everybody could, for we were in full view of a crowd of villagers who had come to see the spectacle of new arrivals — and they'd seen just about everything me and Mam had got!

This introduction to country life began a series of rude awakenings, the next being the pump. There was no running water. It came from a pump outside the back door. When Mam tried to pump some into the small opening of the kettle spout she almost drowned me. Finally I took a cup and got a drink to quieten my sobbing hiccoughs and found it to be cool and pure, better than any tap water I had ever tasted. But I couldn't imagine going out there in the dark for just a cup of water.

At dusk Dad lit an oil lamp which cast eerie, dancing lights across the room. They fascinated and frightened me. I went to bed by candlelight and watched the flickering flame as I sobbed myself to sleep.

The next morning I was sent to school in the hope that I would settle down quicker if I was kept occupied.

Mam was wrong. After Oxford Street school, the village school was just like a dolls house with only two classrooms — one for the under sevens and the other for those up to fourteen years of age. Quickly I began to understand how the evacuees had felt for the children regarded me rather like an alien.

For one thing I was dressed differently. They wore an odd assortment of clothes whilst I wore a school uniform. I spoke oddly to them, with a different accent and much quicker. Also, private education had given me a head start with the lessons and I was far ahead of even the oldest pupil.

In an effort to make friends, I began to tell fibs to try and impress them with stories.

"How is it you know all the answers then?" I was asked.

Shrugging my shoulders I sighed. "Might be because I don't really belong."

"How's that?"

"Well, these people took me in from a big school — after the air raid."

An air raid? Now, that was something. "You been in one?" I nodded.

"You get hurt then?"

And with a quickness that surprised even me, I whipped off my shoe, pulled down my sock and showed my heel operation. They stared in admiration, and it broke the ice and gave me a protection if Dad got drunk and acted daft.

But in all of the two years we lived at Laughton Dad never touched a drop of drink, not once. He dug up the field behind the house and set it with fruit and vegetables. We had pigs and chickens, and two cats. Life, for once, was almost normal.

But I made the mistake of keeping up my inventive stories. Oh, the kids in Brid would have been amazed at the way they appeared in my stories, almost like the Bowrie kids. I would weave tales of adventures that made their hair stand on end. However, fate took a hand, and my series of stories was interrupted by a serious illness.

For weeks I had been getting pains in my legs. Mam said they were growing pains, but one day I was sick as well and Mam decided to keep me at home. The gamekeeper's wife called and remarked how pale I had become and how dark my eyes were. The doctor was called for, but as he only visited once a week, I lay for five days being dosed with castor oil; an old remedy, but it saved my life.

When the doctor finally saw me, he diagnosed rheumatic fever with the added and dreaded complication of St. Vitus Dance. This was considered to be the disease of someone not quite right in the head, because of the muscular spasms. In truth, it is caused by inflamation of the brain through severe rheumatism. The treatment consisted of soft soap baths, wrapping in cotton wool, and then a convalescence of working on the land.

"Get her near the soil, near the iodine and minerals," he told Mam and so she and I went potato picking and earned the princely sum of five shillings for her and two-and-six for me, per day. We worked from eight in the morning until four in the afternoon, and Saturday mornings until noon.

"Head down and arse up," the farmer would shout every morning as the horses ploughed out the rows of white potatoes. We scratted down the sides and picked each one and then after the harrowing we baked some in the burning potato tops. Again life was good.

While I was ill, the schoolmistress came down to see me, or rather Mam.

"I wonder if I could say something to you, Mrs. Clamp, without causing offence."

"I can show you my marriage lines," Mam blurted out.

"Oh, really, how nice. But no, I was wondering about Molly. Is she not your own child?"

"What?"

"Let's start again." And the whole story came out about my fibs. Mam coloured up and came towards me.

"That's not the way to deal with it, Mrs.Clamp." The schoolmistress was a very understanding lady. "I have thought for some time that Molly is far beyond her years. She is far older than she should be, and clever too, and really not learning a lot at the village school. Have you thought about her being privately educated again in Gainsborough?"

Mam pursed her lips and said she would see.

"You know, you might have a writer on your hands. Molly has a vivid imagination."

I didn't quite know what to expect once she had gone. Would I get a good hiding? Mam was very quiet.

"Why did you say that?" she finally ventured.

"Say what?" I parried.

"Say that you weren't mine. Are you ashamed or anything?"

How could I tell her that, yes, I was sometimes ashamed of Dad.

"Well?" she asked again, very near to tears.

"No. I just said it. I saw it in a Shirley Temple picture. It made me cry and I pretended it was me."

She heaved a sigh of relief. "Oh, so, you're not ashamed of me then?"

"Only when you go on about me being best dancer and that. It makes me look daft."

"Well, you're best at fibbing. You can make a story up about a blank page."

Again my fate was decided. I was to go to school in Gainsborough, to a private boarding school, and I was to be a weekly boarder.

"A good education will see that you use your talents," Mam said.

"Not like you, you mean?" I said without thinking.

"Where did you hear that?"

"That bloke, Ralph. He said I was to work hard and not let my talents go to waste, like you had. What's it all about, Mam?"

Mam sighed. "It's a long story and far too much for even your head, my lass. You'll find out one day."

"Shall I get married one day, Mam, and go to dances and that?"

"I shouldn't think anybody would tackle you, and I pity the bloke who does."

Now she was laughing and her laughter made me laugh, too — for once.

CHAPTER ELEVEN

During that summer I seemed to have a lot of time on my hands. I was waiting to go to the Handle House School in Gainsborough and therefore took little interest in what was going on in the village.

Almost to the day of my birthday, there was the evacuation of Dunkirk. We heard about it on the radio, but the events were brought sharply home to us when Dad went out to work one morning and found hundreds of soldiers sleeping on the roadside. He rushed back into the house and told Mam to get the kettle on and then took boxes of eating apples to share out amongst the men. Tea, bread and jam, came from all directions when the women in the village saw what was happening.

The men looked so tired, eyes dark from lack of sleep and the strain they had all been under. They stayed overnight in the village and we put on an impromptu concert which they cheered as we danced and sang. And then, as quickly as they had appeared, they were gone.

I still remember their names — Skipper, Ginger, Lofty and Dusty. In my childish way I fell in love with Skipper who told Mam he had two children of his own. I didn't see how he could, he looked so young.

The officer came to thank us for our hospitality and, smiling at me, he asked, "And what are you going to be when you grow up? Are you going on the stage?"

"No. I'm going to teach and have my own school and then — then I'm going to write."

"Well, you've all the time in the world haven't you: time to grow up, time to pick the flowers. Here, give this to your Mammy." He handed me a blue scabious flower. "Write about us one day, and tell the world what it was really like."

I clutched the flower and waved as they left in a great convoy.

"What have you got there?" Mam asked from the doorway.

50

I lifted up the flower now wilted and bent. "Here, it's for you." Mam took it and smiled. "That officer sent it for you. Said I'd plenty of time, time to pick the flowers, or something."

"You might have hunny, and I only hope to God he has as well." And getting out a tiny vase, she carefully placed the flower on the windowsill where it seemed to perk up and glow, almost like a beacon.

Warnings were issued about spies and infiltrators and we were taught ways of catching them out. One way was to try and get them to say words with "w" as the Germans always pronounced it "v".

One afternoon as Edna Frobisher and I were out for a walk, a young RAF lad stopped and asked the way to the Church. We eyed him suspiciously. In the pictures, spies always made for the church. Edna nudged me. "I'll bet he's one of THEM," she whispered, so we decided to catch him out.

"Do you know the name of the American Secretary of State?" I asked.

The lad looked completely bewildered.

"Go on, say 'Wendle Wilkie'," urged Edna with a menacing look.

He now looked terrified and, jumping on his bike, rode off in all directions.

"I'll bet he was one of them," said Edna. "Shall we tell the gamekeeper?"

The gamekeeper had no authority whatsoever, but he did have a gun, which was more than the Local Defence Volunteers had.

Dad had joined the LDV or the Home Guard as it was called, and maybe it gave him a taste of his army days again. "Any daft bugger can do this bit of a job," he said. "I'm off on munitions at Gainsborough." And he did as he threatened and got a job there at three times his present wages.

Mam was overjoyed. Now I could have all the extras — dancing, singing, elocution, ballet and piano. The old roundabout again.

When it was time for school to begin, my brown portmanteau was packed and I was despatched on the local bus to Gainsborough, getting off at Elm Cottage. Mam had said that someone from the school would meet me, but no one did, so I sat on my case and cried.

A lady rather like Mam came and asked me what was wrong. I told her and very kindly she took me up to the school which was only a hundred yards away, but for all I had known, it could have been a hundred miles away.

Matron took my case and then showed me, with the other new ones, into the dining room. It was tea time. The dining room surprised me as it had trestle tables and forms, a bit like the Salvation Army hall. We said grace and then the headmistress spoke to the new intake.

"We always speak French at the table. As this is your first meal you may use English, but after that it has to be French."

I opened my mouth and then thought better of it. But I was quick to learn. I listened and watched and then mimicked what was said. Soon my plate was full.

"You are doing very well, Molly. Do you speak French?" asked one of the prefects.

I was just about to launch forth on a vivid story of being a refugee, when I thought of the possible consequences. Instead I shook my head.

"Well, I shall put you in for a gold star. That will look good for your house."

I looked up at her and screwed up my eyes in deep thought.

"'House' means, well you'll soon learn. But I'd like you in my house. It's a bit like a team and I can see that you are quick to learn."

It was the first bit of honest praise I had known and I resolved to work harder than ever and get on, like Mam said.

That night, as I sat on my iron bedstead whilst the others were doing their prep, I began to write in my precious exercise book. I would put all my imagination down on paper, it would be safer that way. I wrote, 'The wind whistled through the trees at the back of the big house. It's windy tonight, Shirley said to Jenny her best friend. Yes it is, Jenny agreed.'

I yawned. It had been a long day. I would write more tomorrow.

After that good start, I did well at school. I was good at composition and Mam was pleased with my reports which also always had the rider that if I talked less and worked harder I could be a star pupil!

Dad was still earning good money and Mam decided to go back to Bridlington for a weekend.

By now we were living in East Stockwith at the side of the River Trent and to get to the station we had to be rowed across the river in a rowing boat manned by the local innkeeper, Mr. Allison.

52

I hated that ride. It was six o'clock in the morning, the mist was rising above the water and we could not see the other side of the river bank. We rocked and rolled and I was nearly sick, but we were going home to Brid, and that was almost worth dying for.

Aunt Letty was waiting at the station and I filled with a warm glow as she hugged me closely. My cousin Bertha was also there. Aunt Letty was keeping an eye on her while her husband was away in the army. Mam suggested that she come back with us for a week or two, and then it was decided that I should stay on after the weekend for a week or so to have a bit of a break.

One Thursday night, my cousin Babs and I went to the pictures. We asked Bertha if she would like to come too, but she laughed saying that we were too young for her and she was going out on her own.

Babs and I decided to go to the Lounge Cinema, but half way through the programme I felt uneasy.

"Are you all right?" she asked. I shook my head. "Neither am I," she said. "Come on, let's go home and listen to '*ITMA*'."

We went down the stairs only to find Bertha sitting at the bottom being attended to by a St. John Ambulance man and another of our cousins who was an usherette at the cinema.

"What's up?" Babs asked as she ran down the stairs.

"She's fainted. I should get her home as quick as you can," the ambulance man said.

We got a taxi and took her with us to Aunt Letty's. The doctor was sent for and he diagnosed it as a fainting fit. Two hours later, Bertha died in my aunt's arms.

Babs and I will never know what made us uneasy, nor what made Bertha go from the Regal to the Lounge. We had no idea where she had gone nor did she know which cinema we had chosen. For some weeks before this, Bertha had been worried about not seeing her husband again and we had thought that she felt he was going to be killed. Sadly, she was right and now she would never see him again.

We ran again to 'phone for the doctor, only realising when we hit stones with our feet that we were in our nighties and with no shoes on. I could not believe that anyone could die as young as thirty-three, and I questioned Babs about the whole thing. .

"How did Bertha know where we were?" I asked.

"Something called premonition, or sixth sense. You'll find a lot of it in our family."

The holiday in Brid was shortened, of course, as Mam had to return for the funeral and took me back with her. It was all so sad and as the train pulled out of the station I watched Mam crying bitterly.

After several weeks of feeling off colour, I was taken to the doctor who said I was suffering from anaemia, possibly caused by the shock of Bertha's death or by a lack of vitamins. Because of this, Mam thought it would be better for me to become a day girl at school, so each day, I travelled by courtesy of Enterprise & Silverdawn buses.

And I enjoyed it. I made friends with a family from across the river called Ken and Pat Dixon. I was invited to tea and then to meet Eagre Tide. I had no idea what this was, but I soon found out.

I got into the little boat and then Ken rowed towards the biggest wave I had ever seen in my life. I thought we were going under, but the wave rolled like a great wall and then with a mighty swing we were riding on top. I felt exhilarated — until I heard an angry voice from the bank. It was Mam. She was shouting at the top of her voice that if I got drowned she would kill me. But I was thoroughly enjoying the experience and paid her no attention.

The tide of war was also turning in our favour. Dad had been working for years in the munitions, cycling the seven miles each way to Gainsborough morning and night in all weathers. I had to admit that he was behaving himself and I almost began to trust him. I should have known better.

Each week his firm held a 'Spot the Planes' competition. They all paid a penny and the one who got nearest the number of 'planes to pass overhead won the money, which was quite a tidy sum. Of course, Dad had to go and win it and with his natural talent he got drunk on the winnings.

I wouldn't have minded that so much, but he decided to come home on the bus, the school bus. He was singing at the top of his voice while trying to cuddle me. And then he was sick, in front of all my friends. I was mortified. Finally he fell asleep.

I got off the bus two stops earlier and walked the rest of the way, crying my heart out. Why did he always have to spoil things, and after all this time, and in front of everybody? I would never be able to face them again.

But I had to go to school the next day. They were all very polite,

54

far too well brought up to say anything. But I felt I had to say something.

"He does that sometimes you know. He was tortured at the beginning of the war and sometimes he goes a bit crazy."

Ken's mouth flew open. "Tortured," he gasped.

"Yes, we were living in France when the invasion came and we were caught. That's why I speak such good French. We got away and I was told never to say anything, but I thought you ought to know.

They were all very impressed and took in every word. I did speak quite fluent French and the story fitted, but I was fibbing again, and not for sensationalism. I was fibbing to cover my embarrassment and, in a way, to defend Dad. I couldn't bear for them to laugh at him, in spite of everything.

Dad was given a medical discharge from the munitions and he took a job in the Wolds, Wold Newton to be exact, a small village deep in Lincolnshire.

I became uneasy again. We were on the move and this time to a tied cottage that went with the job. I was fifteen and ready for leaving school and I wondered what life had in store for me this time.

CHAPTER TWELVE

For some reason, Mam decided that I should go to the village school until I thought about what I was going to do. And, to be honest, it was an enjoyable experience. With only four pupils and the teacher, I was almost on a level with her and she in turn was very glad to have me. I was someone to talk to for a change.

The village had a bus twice a week and taps in the street that you had to turn on with a key the size of an axe. We took a bucket twice each day and filled it up. That was the water supply.

"Have you decided upon a career yet, Molly?" Mrs. Day the teacher asked.

I hadn't. I had got the School Certificate and still wanted to teach, but there was little chance of that.

"Why not try commercial college then. There's a very good one in Grimsby. Shall I mention it to your parents?"

Mam was pleased. I could go there for a year and then get a job in an office.

"But I don't want to work in an office. I want to teach and write," I told her for the umpteenth time.

"Them daft ideas. Who's going to pay for it all?"

"Didn't you ever have any ambitions or dreams, Mam? Didn't anybody ever tell you that you were daft?"

She looked crestfallen. "Aye, they did that, and they were right. I've been a fool all my life."

I looked at her then, really looked at her. Her dress was shabby and she looked tired. I knew that Dad's wages were not good, and they were rowing again.

"Oh, all right, I'll go then." I didn't want to upset her any more.

And so I started at Sugdens Commercial School at six-and-sixpence a week. Again it was a miracle how we afforded it. At the college we got typing, shorthand, book-keeping and business training. Just the thing to give me a good start in life. Not a career, mind you. Women didn't have careers. They got a steady job and then married and as soon as they were married they did not go out to work. Work was home and a husband. A good marriage, that was the best thing for a lass

I'll never quite know what that meant. Most of the women I saw looked tired out, shabby, discontented and hard up. I wanted more than that, more than a pinny and a dolly legs wash tub.

But I enjoyed the commercial college and made some very good friends. The typing and book-keeping came easy, but shorthand I could not take in at all and so devised my own.

The war was nearing an end, at least in Germany. The news came through on the radio one afternoon, and Dad opened the window so that some soldiers on manoeuvres could hear the announcement.

Oh, the joy! We danced all night in the village streets to the music of an accordion and we sang and rejoiced for those coming home, and prayed for those still fighting in the east. They were the forgotten army and the one that fought perhaps the most evil and destroying war of all.

A day of national holiday was announced and dances were hastily arranged. Word came down the grapevine, not by 'phone, but by word of mouth, and we chose to go to the dance at North Thoresby.

We biked the seven miles there in all our finery, and of course it rained. I was wearing a crepe-de-chine dress and it got soaked. But the most humiliating thing of all was that the blessed thing shrank up to my behind! Standing in the ladies room we started to laugh. What a sodden lot we looked. But, in the spirit of the day, everyone rallied round and with tugs and pulls we managed to get my dress down to its normal length. Someone produced an iron from the school's domestic room and after two or three glides I was decent.

The music began to tingle in my toes and we danced the night away; waltzes; the jitterbug, where I was thrown through my partner's legs and over his shoulder; quicksteps; and foxtrots. Partners came from all corners of the room and no one was a wallflower that night. I think we danced all the war years away.

I had now begun to notice other girls' way of dressing and hairstyles and I wanted to look like them, even if it meant getting a job to pay for it. The idea quite pleased Mam. Finding the money for the fees had become a burden, that and the bus fares plus pocket money.

57

"What are you going to do then?" she asked.

"Call at the Labour Exchange first and see what they've got."

They were very helpful, particularly when I produced my School Certificate, but very few of the jobs appealed to me. This was a workers time and there was a wide choice of jobs available.

For some reason I opted to be a photographer which meant taking snaps of visitors in Cleethorpes. Why did I chose that? Simply because it offered the most money. After a few days' tuition, off I went. Unfortunately, I was not gifted in that direction, and after many mistakes, the best being a photograph of three legs coming around one corner, I was relegated to the drying room. I didn't like those big drums as they rolled round and round. All I was expected to do was peel off the dried pictures and take them through for trimming. I was bored. So, back to the Labour Exchange.

The next job was in, of all places, a pawn shop. They wanted someone quick with figures and able to keep a check on tickets. And it was good money.

The customers fascinated me. They came in on Monday mornings with their packages for five shillings or so to last them until Friday pay day. Second-hand jewellery made up a lot of the stock and this was bought by the boat skippers for their wives, as a sort of investment.

Just past the shop was a row of cottages where men and women would sit outside weaving the fishing nets. I got to know them well and we would chat for hours whilst I munched my sandwiches at lunchtime.

"I can't think what a lass like you is doing down here," one said. "You speak well, you're well dressed. Why don't you better yourself and get a job in an office?"

I thought about it and realised that the woman was right. I had smartened up considerably for throughout the time I had been working there I had been able to buy some good second-hand clothes that had not been redeemed. They were very good quality and I got them cheap. I often took Mam a dress and things and she, too, began to look a lot smarter.

"I reckon I'm going to try for an office job," I announced at home in my usual forthright manner.

"Oh, aye. Forgotten all about that teaching lark have we?" Dad smirked.

"No. But I can't see how I'm going to do anything about it in this God-forsaken hole." In truth I quite liked the village, but I was just trying to get my own back. So, back once more to the Labour Exchange.

"Aren't you ever going to settle down?" asked the clerk, but offered me a clerk/typist job with the Yarborough Hotel which at that time belonged to the L.N.E.R.

It sounded good, so off I went for the interview. At that time, as labour was in such demand, it could not really be classed as an interview. If you had the necessary qualifications, you got the job.

I liked the Yarborough straight away, with all its red plush and gold. I had never been in an hotel before and everyone was very friendly, and very smart. I put on my best boarding school voice, sailed through the typing test, and was taken on. It was a good wage with the bonus of a hot lunch.

I learned so many things at the Yarborough. I watched the guests, how they dressed and behaved, and I learned to appreciate the fragrant flavour of real coffee. Oh, so sophisticated I was!

My first love affair began there, too. A young naval officer came to stay overnight with his parents and I found every excuse I could to go through the dining room and the lounge if they were there. He would smile and I smiled back. Suddenly, they booked out, and that was that — or so I thought.

That night I went to the pictures and was enjoying Dick Haymes singing *'The More I See You'*, when I felt someone touch my shoulder and a voice whisper, "Parlez-vous Français?"

Turning, my eyes met those of my sailor. I replied in perfect French, which rather took him aback for he, in fact, knew very little French. He had only been trying to impress. We smiled and he came and sat beside me. We held hands and, after the pictures, walked into the dusk of a summer night without having hardly exchanged a word.

"What time is it?"

"Almost eight o'clock."

My last bus went at nine. Ray wanted me to stay, to take a staff room for the night, but Mam would kill me if I wasn't on that last bus.

"Let's go for a drink. I'll pay for a taxi home for you," he said.

Again I shook my head. I knew nothing about taxis or drinks. "I'd

59

rather have a coffee at the bus station."

He smiled down at me. "You're not as worldly as you like to make out, are you. How old are you?"

"Sixteen. How old are you?"

He was nineteen. We went to the little wooden cafe and talked for the rest of the hour. We looked at each other through the smoke and steam, held hands, smiled a lot and trembled.

"I'd best go or I'll miss the bus."

"Look, I'll ride part of the way with you and then get a tram back from Waltham."

I nodded, feeling so happy. We sat on the back seat of the bus and Ray put his arm around me.

"You will write to me won't you?"

I nodded happily. "Where are you going?"

He smiled and touched my nose. Of course, he was not able to tell me that, even though we had won the war.

"I might be able to get away in the morning and have a cup of coffee at the Yarborough."

I thrilled at the thought. The bus reached Waltham and he kissed me. My knees shook and for a few seconds we held each other close, feeling the newness of our emotions — and then he was gone into the darkness.

The next morning I was up early and wore my best suit and blouse.

"What's this then, meeting somebody?" Mam asked.

I smiled in what I hoped was a mysterious way.

"Well, just mind he's not wed, that's all." I could not understand the bitterness in that remark.

The bus was late and fate dealt me a terrible blow. We broke down at Brigsley and I arrived at work in tears. Gladys the receptionist squeezed my hand in sympathy.

"You just missed him love. He waited until the last minute."

Oh, the frustration of it all. I was so in love and left with only a brief memory. It was like the movies.

For three weeks I waited with bated breath for a letter and I knew the minute it arrived, even though I was at work. I hurried home and bounded into the house.

"Is there a letter?"

Mam nodded towards the mantlepiece. I grabbed the blue airmail

60

envelope and stared at the address. Slowly I turned it to open the flap. It had already been opened, very neatly, and stuck down, but nevertheless opened.

Mam busied herself with the meal and I knew she could feel me looking at her. I went up to my room, but somehow the letter had lost its magic. Why on earth had she gone and done that? It was the very first letter I had ever received and Mam had gone and spoilt it all. The contents meant very little, just pleasantries and how glad Ray was that we had met.

"Aren't you coming for your tea?" Mam shouted.

"In a minute."

I couldn't go down just then, I had to compose myself and, not wanting to cause a row, decided that silence would be golden.

But I was seething, and hurt too. This was the first private thing in my life and Mam had to go and interfere. It would be hard to forgive and even harder to understand.

CHAPTER THIRTEEN

Only two more letters came from Ray and I thought he had forgotten me and that perhaps I was just another girl to him. These two letters were never opened by Mam and I always kept them with me for I knew that she would read them if she got the chance.

Mam wanted to know everything about my life and it was as if she was trying to live hers again through me. I sometimes thought that I had lived another life before and I was watching this one from the top of the wardrobe.

On Saturdays a crowd of us went to the Gaiety. It was always packed and we were never short of partners.

"I'd have thought you'd have stayed in now and made things for when he came home," Mam said as she folded her arms and frowned at me as I got ready to catch the bus.

"But I'm not courting or anything. We hardly know each other."

She grunted something about nobody wanting me if I played around. That was a laugh. Who could play around with the last Saturday bus leaving at ten o'clock?

Occasionally I got an ache to see Ray again. I thought that if only we had been able to get to know one another better it could have turned into something quite serious. Maybe he had found someone else. They always said that sailors had a girl in every port.

Coming of age is always an important event in a village and when the postmaster's daughter was twenty-one, and got engaged, they gave a party for the whole village. There was such excitement and I was really looking forward to it. Life was good. I had the thrill of the hotel, city life and rural peace — a bit of everything.

I decided to use some of my precious coupons and make myself a dress.

"Shall I help you? I used to do a lot of sewing," Mam asked as she looked over my shoulder at the blue and white spotted material.

"No thanks, I'll manage," I snapped and then felt sorry when I

62

saw how hurt she looked.

"Tell you what, if I give you the bus fare to come into town on Tuesday, we'll get some stuff to make a frock for you."

She hadn't really made up her mind to go to the party, but this decided her. We got her some floral silk and we set to work making two dresses with every stitch done by hand.

Mine was a plain shirt-waister and Mam made one with tucks and pleats the like of which I'd never imagined. It was a truly professional job, and without a pattern too. It fitted perfectly and she looked a treat.

"I never knew you could do that," I said, and to tell the truth I was a little peeved.

"There's a lot you don't know. I can knit and crochet and all, but what with money and coupons and that, there's never been the chance."

The village tea party was a great success. It was truly a country spread and it was difficult to imagine we had just had a war and were still on rations. There was ham, cakes, trifles, salad, port wine and real butter. I ate as though I had not seen food for years.

Mam pointed to a girl wearing a lovely lacy-patterned twinset. "I could do that, easy as wink," she whispered.

"Do it for me, then. I'll get wool and a pattern."

"Don't need a pattern. Now I've seen it I can do it out of my head."

A few days later I brought home some blue wool and within a week I was wearing a twinset far better than the one we had admired — again without a pattern.

After the tea party we sat and chatted for a while and then decided to go home so that things could be got ready for the dance.

Dad was waiting for us. "Give us five bob, Ada. I'm off up to Clickham. Come on gel, I've not been out for ages."

That was true and Mam rummaged in her purse.

"Oh, go on. I'll give it him." I handed over the money and he pressed my hand.

"I'll give you a kiss then," he said, but I turned away. I hadn't kissed either of them for years, nor they me, come to think of it.

The crafty old devil must have had a bit of brass tucked away for around half-past ten that night he rolled up at the dance, drunk as a lord, with a black eye and a cut cheek.

"He fell off his bike," someone said and laughed.

Dad sat down on one of the desks that had been turned around to serve as a seat and grinned at me.

"Don't want to know your old Dad then. Too high and mighty are we?" his voice slurred across the room.

I wanted to disappear and then I thought to myself, blow it, he's the one who should go. I've nowt to be ashamed of. I walked across to him, took out my hanky and wiped his cheek.

"Now, bugger off home and leave me to enjoy myself." I spoke quietly but very firmly. He looked startled. "You heard, clear off."

"Dance with me first."

He made to grab me and deftly I manoeuvred him to the door. With a hefty shove I pushed him through it

"I told you, clear off. You're not going to spoil my life."

He went into the darkness and I returned to the dance floor to be partnered by an Italian prisoner of war.

"Don't worry about your Papa. He is a good man. He teach me a lot when we work in blacksmith shop together."

This was another side to my father which I had never known.

Handling that situation turned out to be one of the daftest things I had ever done, for Mam began to rely on me more and more as it was obvious that I could cope with Dad. It was like having two bairns around.

It had been so long since I had heard from Ray that I had almost forgotten him. And then a letter came from his mother saying that he had been accidentally killed at sea. The captain had sent his belongings home and included in them were my letters.

It was sad that such a promising young life had been so short and for a while I mourned someone who could have been special to me.

To my amazement Mam sobbed her heart out and she had never even met him. Her explanation was that she felt sorry for his mother, but I felt there was far more to it than sympathy.

"This has got to stop. We've hardly a penny to our names and I'm fed up with struggling. There must be better paid jobs for a bloke like you."

Mam's voice floated up the stairs. My heart sank. Not another move? Again she had made up her mind and soon I was replying for Dad to jobs advertised. One brought an immediate answer from a village near Gainsborough called Willoughton. They wanted an interview as soon as possible.

"You go with him, our Molly. You know better than either of us if it's all right or not. You ask about money and house and that." I hesitated. "Go on, you've got a good head on you and you'll see he doesn't waste the money on drink. He takes more notice of you than he does of me."

And so Dad and I went one Tuesday morning to Lincoln where the farm secretary met us at the station.

Purposely I had dressed in my best tweed suit with matching gloves, shoes and bag. I desperately wanted to give a good impression. The sight of Dad with a young woman suprised the secretary who was a very nice man and once we introduced ourselves he chatted away during the journey to Willoughton.

There was no doubt about it, Dad knew his job all right. He was an excellent tradesman and within only an hour he was offered the job and a house at a much more enhanced wage.

"I'd like to see the house," I said.

Mr. Willimot smiled at me. "And what do you do for a living?"

I explained and he appeared to be impressed. "I'd really like to teach. Teach or write."

He didn't seem to think this was anything out of the ordinary and he startled me by saying, "Funnily enough, there's a college at Lincoln running a scheme for teachers. It's a shortened course, for one year, mainly for people returning from the forces. It was only advertised last night. I'll get the paper for you if you like."

By hek, I would like, very much indeed.

The house was a year old, having been built on old foundations. There was a tap, a sink and a bath in the back kitchen, and electricity. It seemed like heaven.

Mr. Willimot brought the newspaper and then proceeded to tell me all about the village. He had taken to us and I certainly liked the sound of all he was telling me.

I read the advert and wrote in my application. Then Dad and I gave in our notice to leave at the end of the month.

Within a week I received a reply and I was asked to attend an interview. I was over the moon. This must be a good omen and one move that I was going to enjoy.

We settled down almost immediately. It was as if we had finally arrived home. Mam cleaned and decorated the house and took more notice of what was going on.

I attended the interview and was seen by a board of six, four men and two women.

"How long have you had the ambition to teach?" I was asked.

"Ever since I started school and hated it. I've always wanted to make school a place where children would enjoy learning."

"Enjoy?" one of the men asked.

"Well, it strikes me that if they like school then they'll learn. Forcing things into them and not explaining clearly will not get anyone anywhere. If children enjoy something, then they learn."

One woman nodded in agreement.

"Have you any other ambition?" was the next question. Evidently teaching was not enough!

"Yes. One day I'm going to write a book."

They smiled again. "And your own education?"

Good old Mam, I reeled everything off and I could see that they were impressed. I was accepted.

"Have you any particular age group in mind?"

"Nursery, if possible please. I want to be a nursery teacher."

"You sound very definite, young lady, and that is good. We use the Macmillan method, incidentally."

"I don't care what method you use, missus. You just train me and I'll teach." My Yorkshire accent and turn of phrase took them aback.

"And then you will write this book I suppose?"

I sighed. This was daft. "Oh, I'll do that all right. When time comes."

CHAPTER FOURTEEN

As soon as I received my acceptance in writing I told Mam. Her face lit up as I had never seen it for many years.

"I reckon this place is lucky for us," she said.

Unfortunately, Dad was not all that impressed with my achievement. "Have you thought about bus fares and that?"

"Yes. I've got an allowance of nineteen-and-six a week, and I get free dinners."

"Tell you what, I'm earning decent now, I'll clothe you and feed you at home. You earn money for your books and I'll give you some pocket money. When you're finished you can look after us in our old age!"

At the time it seemed like a good proposition.

From the very first day I enjoyed college and teacher training. I made many friends and took note of everything, in and out of lectures.

We dressed very plainly — blouses and skirts, not trousers or jeans or any casual clothing. I had a nice figure and plenty of chance to go out with lads, but none of them attracted me.

"I reckon you'll be an old maid," Mam would say.

"Well, that was our bargain. Molly will look after us in our old age." This came from Dad, jokingly, but Mam was taking it much more seriously.

If I was going out anywhere she would start asking questions. Who with, where, what time would I be home? She didn't feel well, headache, billious, anything she could think of. If it was to do with my training it didn't matter, but if it was just pleasure, then she would create.

I had met a particularly nice girl at college and I was often invited to go to a Saturday night dance and then to stay over. This drove Mam wild and she would try every trick in the book to keep me at home.

A special dance was arranged to be held in the Drill Hall as the Yanks were returning. I didn't care about the Yanks, but I did love dancing and so Audrey and I arranged to go and I would stop over.

"What time will you be back?" Mam asked as I packed my bag.

"Some time on Sunday afternoon."

"I'll wait dinner then."

"Oh, please yourself, Mam. You'd think I was going to the North Pole!"

As I left, she was clutching her heart — but I closed mine and caught the bus.

The dance was super with a big band and lots of partners. I didn't dance with one Yank, but I met a nice lad called Glynn who was in the army and we danced together all night.

As we were having Sunday breakfast, oh so casually in our dressing gowns, Audrey suggested that we go to the local park. Sometimes the soldiers went there for a walk, or to pick up a bit of talent.

"You could catch the five bus. It wouldn't be that late."

After a little thought I agreed. Why shouldn't I have a bit of harmless enjoyment. But I would have to ring and let Mam know.

"You don't have to catch a bus. I'll take you home on the back of my motorbike." This was Audrey's brother and although I'd never ridden pillion before, I agreed for the sheer devilment of it.

We whizzed home across the limestone escarpment with the wind blowing through my hair. Finally, we pulled up with a screech of brakes outside the house. The time was six-fifteen. The village kids gathered round to look at the motorbike, but they got a much more spectacular show than that.

Mam came rushing out of the house like a maniac with her arms in the air as if she was going to clout me. "You little bugger, where have you been? I've been worried sick. I was just going to fetch police."

I was trembling with embarrassment and anger. "I rang Les Ward and sent a message. You knew I was staying on."

She scowled and ignored me. "Who's this then. Bloody motorbikes. Deathtraps they are. Harry Copsey got killed on one." He had lived next door to us in Milner Road in 1937 and had skidded on an icy patch. What had that to do with me now?

I turned to Audrey's brother and apologised.

"Don't worry," he said. "I expect she'll be all right now she sees you're safe."

I smiled weakly and waved him off.

"Where have you been raking about all weekend then?" Mam raged.

"Where's Dad?" I said to try and divert her.

"He went to pub and got a few drinks. He's sleeping it off. You're not going out again my lass."

So that was it. He had got drunk and I had not been there to deal with him.

"No Mam. I'm old enough to please myself and I'll go where I want and when I want. And if you don't agree, then I'll leave home."

"I'll put police on to you."

"What the hell's going on?" Dad poked his head around the kitchen door.

"It's because I'm late home."

"But she knew. Les told me in the pub and I came home to let her know," said Dad.

"Are you sure?" Yes, I could see he was.

When I tackled Mam about it she pretended she hadn't been able to understand him. "He was a bit far gone," she said.

That started them off and another row broke out. I lost my temper.

"Don't you think it's about time you two grew up. What the hell of a kind of life is it for me with all this lot going on? It's a right coming home. You bawl and shout and show me up. It's like a ruddy mad house, and it's been like this all my life. It's the biggest wonder that I'm not barmy."

They stopped dead and stared at me in wonderment. Never before had I turned on them in this way.

"I'm ashamed of you."

That did it. Mam began to cry and Dad hid behind the paper. She wailed and paced up and down the room until I couldn't stand it any longer and I marched out of the back door. I would take a walk around the hill and cool off.

When I got back, Mam had gone to lie down. Mrs. Crowder had come in and was making a cup of tea. She was one of my greatest allies and as I took the cup she winked at me.

"It's nowt. A bit of a tantrum. Go up and see her, but stand your ground. Just be firm and say what you mean."

69

"You've not sent for doctor then?" I asked.

"She's nowt like bad enough for that. She ought to have had a few more kids, that would have settled her."

As I climbed the stairs I was absolutely flaming mad, but decided to take Mrs. Crowder's advice.

"Now look what you've done, you bad girl," wailed Mam. Well, she was strong enough to start calling me names at least.

"I didn't do it, Mam. You did. I've got to live my own life. It isn't as if I go to pubs or out with any Tom Dick or Harry. But I do need friends."

She snorted. "Was it a fellow then. Was that it?"

I shook my head. "Not really. I danced with a lad from Barnsley, a soldier."

I heard a gasp and, looking towards the bed, saw that Mam had fainted. She was out cold. Now what had brought that on?

Mrs. Crowder wetted Mam's lips and brought her round. "Now then, what's all this about?" she asked.

"God alone knows," I snapped and went to my room.

It took about a week for the atmosphere to clear and we were able to speak civilly to one another again. But in spite of the home atmosphere, I worked hard at college and when school practice came along it was a marvellous experience. I loved the children and they, fortunately, appeared to like me.

Mam loved to brag about, "Our Molly, a teacher you know." And in those days teachers were credited with enough brains to know everything. And I mean everything. And, according to Mam, it was all due to her own efforts. She had given up everything to get me in this position. Well, let her think that if she wanted to.

My first teaching post was at a large nursery school in the city, and I loved every minute of it. The whole staff worked as a team and we had a happy establishment in which the children thrived. The deputy head was courting an airman, Ian, who was away and we struck up a firm friendship.

It was through her that I met Cliff Stafford, my first serious romance. He was Ian's friend and they came down one weekend together. We made up a foursome and he was nice. His job had been interrupted by the forces. He had been training to be an architect with the local council near Leeds.

We got along very well and after that first weekend he wrote to me

70

almost every day. I had told Mam all about him — and anyway she knew there was something going on from the letters which kept arriving. In one of the letters he asked me to visit his home.

"Getting serious then?" Mam asked.

I laughed, but I must admit I felt excited. "Not likely. I'm more interested in a career."

I thought Mam might cause a scene, but she didn't. Instead she suggested I ask him home first. "Let's look him over and see if he's good enough," she said.

In for a penny, in for a pound, and so I wrote with the invitation. I worried myself sick all that week. Mam polished and baked as only she could when in the mood, and the whole house was made to feel homely and welcoming.

Cliff duly arrived on the Friday night. The table was laid with all Mam's goodies on it, the hearth was gleaming and Dad sat puffing away on his pipe. It looked like the picture of a perfect home. Introductions were made and we had tea, chatting away as if we had known one another all our lives.

The weekend passed quickly and all too soon it was Sunday and Cliff was away. We had shared long walks and talks. He was going to be demobbed soon and then concentrate on his career.

"I want to be a city architect, it's a great job," he said. "What about your career?"

"I don't honestly know. I've not given it all that much thought."

"Well, think about it now, Molly. I reckon we get along fine and with the possibility of two good careers we could have a good life — a house, holidays and a car. Smashing!"

I thought for a minute. "What about a family and things like that?"

"We'd plan those. I don't fancy a houseful of kids, but one or two planned, that's different."

One thing was for sure, with Cliff I would be safe and secure. His home was upper working class and when I visited we all got along fine. Several times throughout our two year courtship I felt a twinge of uncertainty. I wasn't sure that I wanted to be that organised. It was good to feel secure, but I didn't want everything planned to the last letter. Where was romance?

An engagement was in the offing and Mam pushed it hard. "You're damn lucky to have the chance of a bloke like him. You grab him lass."

And so I did. We got engaged and planned to marry the following Easter Monday. Everyone was thrilled — except me. I was content and secure, but thrilled? No, I certainly was not that.

For about a year I had been singing in a local choir and also taking private singing lessons. One day I was asked to stand in and sing a solo in Handel's *'Messiah', 'He shall feed His flock'*. I was flabbergasted. I had won several musical festivals, but to be asked to sing this was quite an honour.

I practised and practised. Everywhere, you could hear my voice singing away. Mam was more affable now and she made me a lovely black silk dress for the grand occasion.

One Monday morning, coming through the steam of the wash house, I heard Mam's voice. *'He shall feed His flock'*. She was singing it beautifully and far better than I could. Her breathing and intonation were perfect and I felt a bit peeved as I heard her reaching the top notes. But I was too full of excitement to hold a grudge and I soon forgot all about it.

On the great night Mam came with me and I felt good — nervous but good. My hair was nicely permed, my dress of black silk made by Mam felt like a second skin and, to add the finishing touches, I had a small gilt clutch bag and shoes to match.

My nerves twitched as the performance began, but once I stood up to sing, head raised to the great stained glass window, I forgot everything. At least everything except Mam. There she sat, four rows down on the left, arms folded across her chest. As I opened my mouth, she opened hers, and for one awful moment I thought it was going to be a duet! But, thank God, she merely mouthed the words. Good old Mam. What a help she proved to be. I watched her mouth and sang perfectly. My nerves vanished and I heard my voice echo through the church. I ended and looked at Mam. She nodded and I knew I had done all right.

After bowing to the audience I raised my head and looked across into the eyes of a young soldier. He winked and put up his thumb. The other hand was clutching a collection plate.

I grinned back — and fell instantly and hopelessly in love.

CHAPTER FIFTEEN

As quickly as I could I said my farewells for I had something far more important on my mind. From the corner of my eye I spotted the conductor making his way towards me. I dived behind a stone pillar and reeled back in pain as I collided with another body.

"Can't you look where you're going," I snapped.

"Not where you are concerned I can't," came the answer from my soldier.

It was as if we had known each other all our lives and I was on cloud nine, until I spotted Mam waiting for me.

"Can't stop now. There's my mother waiting and our bus goes in half-an-hour."

He looked downcast. "I'll walk with you."

I frowned. What would Mam have to say about that? But I felt such excitement that I threw caution to the wind and accepted his offer.

"What's your name?" I asked.

"Pete, Pete Stevens." It had a nice ring to it.

"Mine is ....," and he laughed. Of course, he knew my name from the programme.

I got my things together and went to the main doors to find Pete and Mam talking away.

"This young chap enjoyed your singing." Mam smiled and without any further ado we all started walking down to the bus station. Pete was chatting away to Mam who was actually chatting back, and, more than that, enjoying herself.

When we reached the bus station he took my elbow as Mam walked on. "See you tomorrow, outside the theatre in Scunthorpe?"

I looked surprised. "O.K.?" he hesitated.

"O.K." I answered firmly.

As we journeyed home I turned to Mam and said, "Did you enjoy it then. Did I do all right?"

She gave one of her most stunning answers that only Mam could give. "Well," she deliberated for a moment. "Thank God I wasn't shamed on you." Praise indeed.

"Who was that lad then?" she asked, but not unpleasantly.

"Don't really know. I only met him tonight. His name is Pete Stevens."

"Hmmm. Don't forget you're engaged."

How could I?

That first date was terrific. It was obvious that we both felt the same way about each other and had eyes for no one else. And, what was more important, we actually liked each other and had a great deal in common. He, too, was an only child of elderly parents.

As he kissed me good night he whispered, "See you tomorrow." It was a statement, not a question.

I shook my head and held out my left hand to show the tiny sapphire ring.

"Yes, I know. But you can't go through with that now, can you?"

I knew I couldn't. It didn't matter whether I saw Pete again or not as far as that was concerned. I knew that if I was so interested in someone else then Cliff was not my great romance.

"Don't worry, we'll sort something out," and he smiled as we parted.

As soon as I turned the corner of Middle Street the next night I knew something was going on. My sixth sense told me that it was to be a momentous night.

Warily I opened the door to find Pete sat there with Mam and Dad, and chatting away as easily as if he was one of the family.

"You can come in, our Molly. This young man tells me you and he are taken." I smiled at the old fashioned phrase Dad was using.

I had to nod in agreement. At the same time I looked sideways at Mam. This could be a whopper of a row.

She sighed and nodded too. "I could see it the minute you met. And it's no good if you're not sure about Cliff. And what about him? Aye, you'll have to tell him."

This was something I couldn't believe. Pete Stevens must have a way with him to charm Mam and Dad in such a short time. I learned that he had been there almost all the afternoon. He'd obviously charmed Mam first. What an approach!

"I'll write to Cliff. I'll do it tonight."

"No you won't. You'll face him with it. That way you'll know if you're doing the right thing," Mam commanded and who was I to argue.

Cliff took it very well. I don't think he was really in love with me. I was more like a good investment.

But as for Pete Stevens, he was something else and we were madly in love for all the world to see. Three weeks after we met he proposed and we were engaged and sixteen weeks to the day we met, we were married.

Oh, it wasn't all easy. Mam played up when she realised that things were serious. Pete's parents were not all that pleased either, not once they had met Mam and Dad. I think they liked me at first, but when Mam put on her best hostile look and Dad just gave up and went to the pub as soon as he could, they began to think differently.

I was driven to church in a Rover car by the local headmaster. Dad held my hand tightly.

"You are sure about this, Molly?" he asked.

I nodded and smiled through my white veil.

"It can be good, you know. Don't take all that much notice of your Mam. It ain't always been like this for us." His eyes filled with tears and held a faraway look. I touched his hand and he smiled. "Come on then, gal. Head up, shoulders back, be proud."

'Love Divine All Loves Excelling'. I heard the music as I entered the tiny Willoughton church and then my eyes met Pete's and, as on that very first meeting, I forgot everything else.

And where do you think we spent out honeymoon? Why, in Brid, with dear old Aunt Letty, and we had a whale of a time. Not the conventional honeymoon, but nevertheless a memorable one.

Pete was still in the army and so that we could get a place of our own he decided to sign on. There was no privacy with Mam and Dad. We had to talk in whispers, and as for love making, those old bed springs advertised to the whole street what we were up to.

Fate gave us a great help by posting him to Norwich. We talked it over and decided that we would try for a flat. I would get a teaching job there and we would start our married life properly.

He left on the Thursday and I missed him dreadfully. He wrote asking me to go down for a weekend as his mate was being posted and there was a flat in the offing.

It was bliss. We stayed in a tiny guest house and for the first time

75

knew what privacy meant. The flat, too, was ideal. Small and compact and just what we needed.

As I journeyed home I began to worry about Mam. She was sure to play up and I didn't want anything to spoil things, not now. But fate has so many hands, some good and others, well, not worth thinking about.

As I walked around the corner, I saw Dr. Neal's car outside our home. The nurse arrived at the same time as I did. The house was full, or so it seemed, full of neighbours and Mrs. Crowder busily making tea and whispering to Dad.

"Oh, good, you're here. Your mother has suffered a serious heart attack. She will need constant attention and care. It's a good job you are living at home. The district nurse is busy enough as it is."

No question about it. It was my duty and that was that. It was not only expected but accepted that a daughter should stay at home and look after ailing or elderly parents. It was something I never came to terms with. I knew in my heart that Mam really had a heart condition, nobody could be that good an actor, but I was just as ruddy sure that she had brought a lot of it on herself by getting in such a state. Why was she so bitter, why so afraid of my leaving? What had made her marriage go so wrong, although that wasn't quite the right word. It hadn't exactly gone wrong, it was as if it had never happened. It was just an empty void. I prayed that mine would not go the same way.

Dad sat by the fire, puffing away at his pipe. "I'm sorry, Molly," he sighed. I felt he understood, that he knew all our plans. He was truly sorry, but that was no use at all.

My life stretched before me like a black chasm.

CHAPTER SIXTEEN

I rang Pete in a flood of tears. He tried to comfort me by saying that he would come back at the weekend and sort something out.

"You can stop with us and he can stop in army and come home on leave," Mam said, sitting up in bed drinking a cup of tea.

I scowled. "That's not what I want from marriage. That's no sort of life. Would you have had that, Mam, would you?"

She sighed heavily, but could not meet my eyes.

"Haven't you ever loved anyone Mam, really loved them? Anybody except yourself." I asked bitterly.

Suddenly she banged down her cup and started waving her arms about. "You don't know what you're talking about my lass. I could tell you. I could. Oh, go away. You'll only make me bad again."

The heaving and sighing returned, and I got frightened in case it brought on another heart attack. I could not bear the responsibility of that.

Pete came and we talked long into the night, deciding that he would go back into his father's business. We would get a house in his home village to the south of the county and try to make some sort of a life for ourselves. Life? That was a joke.

Dad's eyes flinched when I told him of the plan. "What's up now. Doesn't that suit?" I snapped.

He looked across at me with those half-closed eyes. "It's nowt. I once worked near there, that's all."

Pete's parents were none too pleased either. They welcomed their son back into the business, but they weren't too keen on the encumbrances of Mam and Dad.

I decided that once we settled down, I would get a teaching job, perhaps in the village school. I began to look forward to the move. At least the house would be mine and Pete's. How wrong I was. My inlaws took over, chose the house and bought it. I never even saw it until it was all arranged. It turned out to be a tiny cottage, just big enough to house the four of us.

We settled down to an uneasy peace. I applied for a teaching job, but just before the interview I found out that I was pregnant. Pete was over the moon, but I was not so sure. I couldn't help feeling that this would be yet another bone of contention.

We had a lovely eight pound daughter whom we called Elaine. We even had a row with both sets of parents about her name, but I stuck to my guns. Mam rallied round a bit and began to help around the place, until I realised that she was trying to take over my daughter. But there was no doubt that my daughter and her Granny had a great affection for each other.

Three years later our son was born and again he fell under the spell of Granny and Pops. They spent hours together the four of them, playing and singing. I almost envied the relationship and wondered why it couldn't have been like that for me.

Only once in ten years did Pete and I manage to get out together, to a reunion dinner. On our return we were met with a whole list of complaints and decided that it was better to stay at home and have less hassle.

"I never left you, never. You should stop at home and look after your own bairns," Mam shouted.

"It might have been better if you had left me and let go of the apron strings a bit. Dad might have had a better life then," I snapped back.

Dad smothered a snigger with a cough and splutter and Mam was furious and told me I didn't know it all yet. I wished I did!

We lived together for over ten more years. So much for a heart condition. I tried to keep the peace and so did Pete. But happiness? That was something I felt I would never know. I felt sorry for Pete. He had been denied a normal married environment with his wife and children. I felt that I didn't really know him. We were never alone long enough to find out what we were really like deep down inside.

When my son was nine, we gave him a birthday party. Mam usually loved them and would throw herself, heart and soul, into the preparations. This time, she didn't seem quite so keen.

"I'm not feeling well," she said.

I looked at her and saw that she was very pale, almost yellow, and her eyes had sunk into her head. I had not noticed it before and I felt guilty. "Shall we have doctor?" I asked.

78

"Wait a bit first. It might go off."

But it didn't and when she finally allowed me to get the doctor in, cancer of the bowel was diagnosed.

"What about a specialist?" I asked.

He shook his head. "Too far gone for that." I told him how stubborn she had been about calling him in. "Wouldn't have made any difference at her age and the sort of cancer it is. Don't blame yourself at all."

As the doctor left I could hear Mam upstairs, singing softly to herself, *'When the poppies bloom again'*.

I went to tell Dad, the only way I knew, by writing it down on a piece of paper. He put on his glasses, took the paper and read it slowly. With shaking hands he threw it on to the fire and nodded at me. He stared into the fire as the flames devoured the paper and the look in his eyes told me that he was miles away. A solitary tear fell down his nose and tentatively I held out my hand, but with a wave he brushed it away.

"Don't bother, it's all right," he whispered.

Throughout the following weeks Pete and the children became a tower of strength. Dad was good, but now, at almost eighty-two, there was little he was capable of doing. He went for walks as if to try and get away for a while, perhaps to lose himself in memory.

It was during one of Dad's walks that Mam began to talk to me.

"You know I was married before?" she started, blunt and to the point as only Mam could be.

"Before what?" I parried, not sure that I wanted a heart to heart at that moment.

"Before your Dad," she spoke impatiently. I nodded. "He was a good lad was Wilf."

For the next hour and a half she poured out her heart, skirting briefly around the bigamous marriage she and Dad had had and dwelling on her little Wilf who had been "Taken before his time."

We laughed and cried together and Mam's face showed shadow and shine, a Mam so engrossed in her story that I did not seem to count.

"I want you to do something for me, promise" She grabbed my hand and without waiting for an answer she made me promise that every November 11th I would, no matter where I was, place a wooden cross in a Garden of Rememberance. The cross was to bear

79

Wilf's name, rank and number, regiment and decoration. "He must never, never, be forgotten," she said.

I learned during that long talk that every year without fail she had sent five shillings back to Brid for flowers and a cross to be laid at the Cenotaph. I could not believe that it was possible for me to spend a lifetime with someone and yet know so little about them.

I asked why she had spurned Ralph, whom I could vaguely remember. "I don't reckon I was ever cut out to be a lady, and anyway, your Dad was all right in them days," she laughed.

"So you did feel something for Dad?"

Mam pursed her lips. "Course I did. But well, things get a bit lost, don't they, as time goes on. We've been all right."

All right? That wasn't the word I would have used to describe what they had been through.

She hutched herself across the bed and touched my arm. "Don't think me daft, our Molly, but I never believed Wilf was really killed. I always felt he would come back, crippled or shell-shocked, and he wouldn't let me know, him not wanting me to see him like that."

"Didn't you try the Red Cross or anything?" I asked.

Her eyes brightened. "They had so much on their plates just then. But you do it for me. Do it now."

And so, nearly fifty years after Wilf was killed, I wrote to the Red Cross. Within days we received a reply saying that he had been reported missing with no known grave. But his name was on the Menin Gate. They said Mam could go if she wished on one of the War Graves Commission visits.

"I'd have liked that," she sighed. "Tell you what, you go. Go and lay a white rose for Yorkshire for me."

Foolishly I made the promise with no thought of ever being able to keep it.

Three days later she fell into a coma. I took her up a cup of tea one morning and found that she had drifted into a world of her own. I was her sister Lizzie and all through that day she was with Wilf and her family. Time and time again she called out for her Dad and then, surprisingly, with my name on her lips, she died.

"Molly, Molly, you've been an angel to me." These were the last words she spoke.

I went downstairs and told Dad. "She's gone," I whispered, holding his hand.

"I know, I know," he said. "I can't cry any more, and you've no need."

He was too frail to attend the funeral and so it was Pete, the children and I who followed Mam. The children were heart-broken that Granny Ada would not tell them any more stories of her life as a little girl, or sing with them, or recite her epic poems that made them laugh so much. I felt sad, nothing more. Sad, but relieved that so much suffering had finally ended.

Dad was very brave and one afternoon as we sat chattering he told me about his life, or at least part of it. It would have taken another lifetime to relate it all.

"I loved Ada, really loved her," he said. "But as usual, I was daft and threw it all away. Ada didn't forgive things like that. You're a lot like her really. Not in your looks, but in your ways. And sometimes when I watched you, it reminded me of...." His voice faded away.

I had to turn away. What a waste of two no three lives, for I felt that mine, too, had been sacrificed.

I had put a notice of Mam's death in the Brid papers and I was surprised to receive a letter only a few days later from Ralph Pinkney. Enclosed was a cheque for a wreath. In the simple letter he said how he had known Mam for years and had admired her spirit and charm I was to buy a wreath and inscribe it 'With highest regard, an old friend.' I did this, but I never said anything to Dad about it.

Quietly, one December afternoon, I went to the village cemetery and laid the wreath. I can't explain why, but it was as if I was saying goodbye to a long lost love. I was playing a part, caught up in a drama over which I had no control.

Exactly sixteen weeks after Mam died, to the exact hour and day, Dad passed away in a peaceful sleep.

On the morning of the funeral our local doctor came to see if I was coping. He looked at the drawn curtains and the food laid ready for the usual tea after the service and said, "You've had a rough time, young lady. I want you to promise me that when this lot is over you will have a good night's sleep, get up in the morning, open these curtains and live."

I brightened. I could do that now, couldn't I? I was a free agent. I could wash when I wanted, clean the house as I liked, do things in my home that suited me. I was free, really free.

I went through the motions of the funeral service, sat through the

81

tea party and watched Dad's sons mourn. I mourned too, in a way. Mourned for a life that was lost, a life that cost so much more than just death. Just think, if little Wilf hadn't been killed, none of this would have been.

I started my life of freedom by spring cleaning. The kids helped me and Pete laughed at my enthusiasm.

Six weeks after Dad died I got a letter from a firm of solicitors in Brid saying that Ralph Pinkney had died and left me a large sum of money.

Pete frowned as I showed him the letter. "Well?" he asked.

"I'm going to send it back. It wouldn't be right, not to Dad, and I'm damn sure Mam wouldn't have taken it."

Pete beamed. "That's my girl," he laughed.

"No, that's Ada's girl," I murmured and I could almost feel Mam chuckling.

I was beginning to feel more kindly towards my parents. I was still bitter about the lost years, but I felt more kindly now that I knew more of their situation. It was quite a story.

CHAPTER SEVENTEEN

After a few months of decorating and moving furniture about the house, it felt more like my own home. But in spite of this, Pete and I became unsettled. His father talked of retiring and handing over to Pete, but he did not want that. He, too, wanted his freedom, a chance to try his hand at a profession.

A chance came through the Civil Service which meant a move to Lincoln and a lower income, but we took the risk. We bought a big family house and soon all settled into city life.

I looked around for a job in a private school and then got the idea of starting my own playgroup. I opened up with five children in the front room of our house. It grew into a thriving nursery school which, with my qualifications, was possible, and as we grew we moved into a disused school. Soon there were sixty children, a long waiting list, six teachers and a secretary.

The sessions were only for half a day in the morning and now that I had help in the house I found I had time on my hands and became restless again. "Not enough to occupy your mind," as Mam would have said.

One of the parents gave me a contact for a newspaper and soon I began to write a small column. I really did enjoy myself and soon I was offered a more permanent position. I decided to close the school and take up journalism full time, but on a freelance basis. This in turn took me into advertising and public relations. I loved meeting people and the contacts I made in the various organisations and societies.

Pete, too, was doing well and the children were growing up into nice kids and giving us lots of pleasure through their friends and hobbies.

It was through one of my contacts that Pete and I were invited to attend a regimental dinner of old comrades. We were both patriotic and with a night of memories of the war we had a great time. There was to be a visit to Dunkirk to celebrate the fortieth anniversary of the evacuation and we were asked if we would like to go. I wonder what Mam would have had to say about us going abroad?

"Go on, there'll be a lot more of us, from Grimsby, Scunthorpe, Louth, Hull and all over the place," we were told.

What an opportunity. We couldn't miss that. My newspaper was delighted and it was agreed that I would do all the reporting and Pete was organised to take the photographs.

We watched the parade in Dunkirk and attended the beachhead service. I saw men in tears, bending down to touch the place from which they had escaped all those years ago.

A trip to the military cemetaries had been arranged and I stood and stared at the row upon row of white crosses. Many were simply inscribed with the words, 'The body of an unknown British soldier'. Wilf could be there. I thought.

And then we were taken to the Menin Gate. Pete and I searched for Wilf's name and we finally found it — Wilfred Tanner, M.M.

In my hand I clutched a white rose, the rose of Yorkshire. As I bent forward to lay it beneath Wilf's name, the sound of the Last Post rang through that great arcade of names. I thought I was dreaming and then I realised it was a nightly ritual in this Belgian town.

With tears rolling down my cheeks I stood in silence with Pete at my side standing to attention. This was Wilf's funeral. I had finally laid him to rest for Mam's sake, and my own too.

Hand in hand Pete and I went to look for his name in the Book of Rememberance. Under the next of kin column was Mam's name, Ada Tanner, widow, 64 St. John Street, Bridlington. These few words held a lifetime.

As we stood there, I felt a hand upon my shoulder and turned to look at a tall man aged about sixty who somehow looked familiar. He held out his left hand, the right sleeve hanging empty.

"Aren't you that little lass from the village? Your Dad gave us some apples. I'm Skipper. Remember me?"

Of course I remembered him. We hugged each other like long lost friends, perhaps glad to see that we had both survived.

"Written any books yet?" he laughed.

I shook my head and told him that I was doing the next best thing, being a journalist.

As our bus arrived to take us away, Skipper asked, "What lot are you with then?"

I told him and was surprised to learn that he was from the Grimsby branch of the same division. We arranged to meet at the October reunion dinner.

Next day I stood at the barriers and watched the big parade which took place in the little Belgian town of Le Panne. The whole town closed down to pay tribute to those who had fought.

The parade came round the corner headed by six British policemen who marched their hearts out. Then followed a Scottish pipe band and I watched with pride as the 'Ladies from Hell' swung their kilts in time to the beat of the drum. Next came an ex-Guards officer, bowler hat solidly in place, umbrella reversed under his arm with the other swinging in such precision that I cheered. He headed the columns of marching men, thousands of them, medals gleaming in the Belgian sunshine. Irish, Australian, Canadian and the British Tommy, oh how they marched and how we cheered. I have never felt such overwhelming pride. It must have been an emotion such as this that made all those lads enlist in 1914. And then I thought of all those crosses. Was it worth it? Shall we ever know?

Throughout the following months I felt an urge to put down on paper the story of Mam and her family. But there were a lot of gaps to be filled and I only had memory to go on, memory and a lot of overheard conversations.

"It would make a good serial," Pete said. But who would want to hear the ramblings of my memories.

The Regimental Dinner was nearing and I made a book of all the pictures that Pete had taken at the Dunkirk anniversary and I added my press cuttings and some of my own thoughts. I had also added a poem which they asked me to read out as a tribute. I presented them with the book and read the poem:

Were you at Dunkirk I asked the man?
Did you see the carnage there?
The death, the smoke, the horrendous noise,
Did you face death with a stare?

It happened so very long ago
It's hard at times to recall
To remember how bravely those young men stood,
Yes, stood to the very last call.

To those who came back it was like a bad dream,
The scene of a horror film set.
But those who came back still remember it well,
And promise — lest we forget.

I met Skipper in the bar and he said how much he admired the poem and the book. "But what about you? You said you were going to write," he teased.

I smiled mysteriously and said, "Wait and see."

I had made up my mind. The following week I contacted Radio Humberside and talked to Graham Henderson who agreed to read the serial. But I hadn't written it yet! It was all in my head. Where would I start? At the beginning with Granny and Grandad. I could hear Mam telling me what to do. What would I call it. An old family saying came to mind, "I'm fed up to the top attic." That was it. It would be fiction based on fact and that would give me licence to fill in the gaps, to weave them in and out into a story.

I started the research and found so many coincidences in my life: Dad marrying Kathleen only a few miles from where he was buried, the marriage that caused so much trouble later; and how I was born, several years later, but to the very hour on the day and date that Wilf had been killed.

I would weave it all in and out and make a story which might make a book. Now I had the time, time to pick the flowers, to smell the scent of memory.

A bouquet for Mam.